C000151245

THE BE

The Best of John Bunyan

Edited by Robert Backhouse

Hodder & Stoughton

LONDON SYDNEY AUCKLAND

British Library Cataloguing in Publication Data
A record for this book is available from the British Library

ISBN 0 340 65633 6

Typeset by Watermark, Cromer, Norfolk
Printed and bound in Great Britain by
Cox & Wyman, Reading, Berks

Hodder and Stoughton Ltd
A Division of Hodder Headline PLC
338 Euston Road
London NW1 3BH

Contents

Introduction

John Brown, one of John Bunyan's successors as minister of the church in Bedford, concludes his unsurpassed biography of Bunyan by suggesting how we can benefit from Bunyan's life.

There remains but the expression of the hope that we may each of us take to his own life the lesson of the life-story we have followed; the lesson that through all opposing forces of ill we should each be true to our better selves, true to the light which comes to each man from heaven, and true to the generation in the midst of which it was ordained that our own life-work should be wrought. The history of the past fails of its deepest purpose if it holds up no guiding light to the present.

In stirring lines called forth by the Bunyan Celebration of 1874, it may be said that:

To deal with the Past is of small concern;
That light for the day's life is each day's need,
That the Tinker-Teacher has sown his seed;
And we want *our* Bunyan to show the way
Through the Sloughs of Despond that are round us
     today,
Our guide for struggling souls to wait,

And lift the latch of the wicket-gate.
The churches now debate and wrangle,
Strange doubts theology entangle:
Each sect to the other doth freedom grudge,
Archbishop asks ruling of a judge.
Why comes no pilgrim, with eyes of fire,
To tell us where pointeth minster spire,
To show, though critics may sneer and scoff,
The path to 'The Land that is very far off'?
The people are weary of vestment vanities,
Of litigation about inanities,
And fain would listen, O Preacher and Peer,
To a voice like that of this Tinker-Seer;
Who guided the Pilgrim up, beyond
The Valley of Death, and the Slough of Despond,
And Doubting Castle, and Giant Despair,
To those Delectable Mountains fair,
And over the River, and in at the Gate
Where for weary Pilgrims the angels wait![1]

Bunyan's spiritual quest

Bunyan's character was complex, and his life was turbu-
lent. It is not accurate to write him off as an 'unlettered
tinker from Elstow'. Rather than picturing him as an
ignorant gypsy, we would do better to think of him as a
godly theologian who spent most of his time studying the
Scriptures so that he could teach his family, his friends and
his congregations about God's grace in Jesus Christ that he
had discovered for himself. As David Marshall has pointed
out, 'Bunyan's closely-argued exposition of Pauline theology to be found in *Pilgrim's Progress Part I* following Christiana's Calvary, would bear comparison with that of the
great Independent theologian Dr John Owen, Bunyan's
friend and champion'.[2]

Much of Bunyan's writing is in the realm of the imagination, allegory and dreams. These were more than a literary

genre, they were reflections of Bunyan's own spiritual conflicts. He was naturally prone to waking dreams and visions. As John Brown emphasises:

There are some natures to whom the great spiritual world of the unseen is always present as the background of life. It was so with Shakespeare. It was so with Bunyan, though in a different way. Even when he was a child, the wrong things of the day were followed by the remorse, and fears, and dread dreams of the night. But the real struggle began later, when after his marriage and reading of his wife's books, he was seen 'going to church twice in a day, and that with the foremost'.

He had not done this long before there arose a fight with his conscience about Sunday sports, in the course of which there came the weird voices that seemed to be shouted into his ear on Elstow Green. Somewhere on the sward round the broken pillar of the old Market Cross he was one Sunday in the midst of a game of cat [a forerunner of cricket]. He had struck it one blow from the hole and was about to strike it a second time, when, he says, 'A voice did suddenly dart from heaven into my soul, which said, Wilt thou leave thy sins and go to heaven, or have thy sins and go to hell? At this I was put to an exceeding maze. Wherefore, leaving my cat upon the ground, I looked up to heaven, and was as if I had with the eyes of my understanding seen the Lord Jesus looking down upon me, as being very hotly displeased with me.'

Strange alterations of gloom and glory came over him. Sometimes his soul was visited with such visions of light and hope that he could have spoken of God's love and mercy to the very crows on the ploughed land before him.

One day as he was passing into the field, still with some fears in his heart, suddenly this sentence fell into his soul:

'"Thy righteousness is in heaven." And methought withal I saw with the eye of my soul, Jesus Christ at God's right hand. I saw, moreover, that it was not my good frame of heart that made my righteousness worse; for my righteousness was Jesus Christ himself, the same yesterday, today, and for ever. Now did my chains fall from my legs indeed; I was loosed from my afflictions and irons. Oh, methought, Christ! Christ! There was nothing but Christ himself that was before my eyes!'[3]

The times Bunyan lived in were an age of intolerance. Anyone who refused to follow the order of service in the Book of Common Prayer risked imprisonment. Bunyan was arrested on 12 November 1660 after he had preached to a small group of people in a private house. During his twelve-year-long imprisonment he probably only had a copy of the Bible and Foxe's Book of Martyrs to read. As John Brown puts it, 'Bunyan took in with him two familiar friends. "There also," says his visitor, "I surveyed his library, the least and yet the best that ever I saw, consisting only of two books – a Bible and the Book of Martyrs."'[4]

In a subsequent and up-dated edition of Foxe's book, Bunyan's imprisonment is one of the very few entries about people who were not eventually martyred. The entry reads as follows:

On the 12th November, 1660, he had arranged to meet a small congregation, in a house at Samsell, in Bedfordshire, but before the time appointed he was informed that a warrant had been issued for his seizure. The danger did not cause him to swerve from what he believed to be the path of duty. He was accordingly arrested at the meeting, but not before he had uttered the following words: 'You see we are prevented of our opportunity to hear the Word of God, and are likely to suffer for the same; but be not discouraged: it is a mercy to suffer for so good a cause. We might have been apprehended as thieves and murderers, but, blessed be

God, it is not so. We suffer as Christians for well-doing; and better to be persecuted than the persecutors.' After being taken before a magistrate, he was committed for trial at the next sessions, when he was indicted for 'devilishly and perniciously refraining from coming to church, to hear divine service; and for being an upholder of conventicles, to the great disturbance of the good subjects of this kingdom, and in contradiction to the laws of the king.' On this charge he was convicted, and sentenced to imprisonment, with an intimation that if he did not conform within a given time, he should be banished out of England. In prison he suffered much, for it was very damp – so damp, that Bunyan said it was enough to 'make the moss grow upon his eyebrows'.

Had Bunyan promised not to preach, he would have been set at liberty, but he thought it was his duty to suffer for Christ's sake, and 'he endured as seeing him who is invisible'. Bunyan had no library to refer to while he was writing: his Bible and an old concordance were the only books he had; and he was reduced to such a state of poverty, owing to his long imprisonment, that his blind daughter used to knit stay-laces, her father, 'the immortal tinker', tagged them, and the poor wife used to sell them in the streets. . . . Had not Bunyan been cruelly cast into Bedford gaol, *The Pilgrim's Progress* might never have been written.[5]

Grace Abounding

During his imprisonment Bunyan published nine books.

This anthology of Bunyan's writing starts with extracts from *Grace Abounding*, or, to give it its full title, *Grace Abounding to the Chief of Sinners, or, A brief relation of the exceeding mercy of God in Christ to his poor servant John Bunyan*. Published in 1666, this is Bunyan's spiritual autobiography, and has been favourably compared with

Augustine's *Confessions*. In it we are given the highest
expression of Bunyan's religious vision. Its record of his
inner life anticipates the dramatic imagery of his later
renowned allegory. Thus *Grace Abounding* serves as a valu-
able introduction to *The Pilgrim's Progress*.

The Pilgrim's Progress

Altogether John Bunyan wrote sixty-two books, but he is
remembered for one: *The Pilgrim's Progress* (1678). An
abridged and updated edition of this now follows in this
anthology. After the Bible, *The Pilgrim's Progress* probably
remains the most widely read Christian book of all time.
By 1885 the list of translations of it read as follows: *British
Isles:* Welsh, Gaelic, Irish; *Northern Europe:* Dutch, Danish,
Swedish, Norwegian, Icelandic, Russian, Lithuanian, Esto-
nian, Finnish, Lettish; *Central and Eastern Europe:* German,
Czech, Hungarian, Serbian, Bulgarian; *Southern Europe:*
French, Italian, Spanish, Portuguese, modern Greek;
Asian: Hebrew, Arabic, Armeno-Turkish, Greco-Turkish,
modern Syriac, Persian, Pasthu or Afghani, Urdu or
Hindustani, Roman Urdu, Persian Urdu, Bengali, Uriya
or Orissa, Hindi, Sindhi, Punjabi, Telugu, Canarese,
Tamil, Malayalam, MarathiBalbodh, Gujerati, Singhalese,
Assamese, Khasi, Burmese, Sgau-Karen, Dyak, Malay,
Japanese, Chinese; *Africa:* Sechuana, Xhosa, Sesotho, Efik,
Otyiherero, Ashante, Duala, Yoruba; *Pacific islands:*
Malagasy, Raratongan, Tahitian, Maori, Fijian, Hawaiian,
Aneityumese; *American:* Mexican, Cree and Dakota.

Many people have tried to account for the popularity of
The Pilgrim's Progress. Hippolyte Taine writes: 'The reason
for *Pilgrim's Progress* being the most widely read book in
England, after the Bible, is that the basis of Protestantism
is the doctrine of salvation by grace, and that no writer has
equalled Bunyan in making this doctrine understood.'[6]
Dean Stanley, at his address at Bedford in 1874, refers
to the work's influence as 'one of the few books which act

as a religious bond to the whole of English Christendom
. . . which has contributed to the common religious culture
of the Anglo-Saxon race.'

Coleridge wrote on the flyleaf of his copy, 'I know of no
book, the Bible excepted as above all comparison, which I,
according to my judgment and experience, could so safely
recommend as teaching and enforcing the whole saving
truth according to the mind that was in Christ Jesus, as *The
Pilgrim's Progress*.'

Macaulay pointed out that it was the only book of its
kind that possessed a strong human interest – that 'while
other allegories only amuse the fancy, this has been read
by thousands with tears'. Macaulay was not one to stint
praise of *The Pilgrim's Progress*, as is illustrated by his
famous words, 'We are not afraid to say, that though there
were many clever men in England during the latter half of
the seventeenth century, there were only two great cre-
ative minds. One of those produced *Paradise Lost*, and the
other *The Pilgrim's Progress*.'

The enormously popular nineteenth-century Baptist
preacher, C. H. Spurgeon, told the theological students at
his Pastors' College that he had read and re-read *The Pilgrim's Progress* more than one hundred times, and that he
benefited from reading it in a different way each time he
read it.

Only a few years ago, when Terry Waite lay handcuffed
to a radiator in an unknown location in Lebanon, he
received one communication. He was sent a postcard of a
stained glass window depicting Bunyan looking through
the window of his prison cell. This postcard greatly
encouraged him in his fearful ordeal.

When John Bunyan was in prison he sent letters to his
Bedford brethren to comfort them. Extracts from *A Relation of the Imprisonment of Mr Bunyan* (first published 105
years after it was written) now follow in this anthology,
revealing how Bunyan tried to comfort those outside
prison who were concerned for him.

The Pilgrim's Progress (Part II) was first published six years after Part I, in 1684. It describes the adventures of Christian's wife, Christiana, her children and her friend Mercy on their pilgrimage. In the extracts selected in this anthology from Part II we view more mysteries at Mr Interpreter's house, walk in the company of Mr Greatheart and cross the river with Christiana.

Other writings

After *Grace Abounding* and *The Pilgrim's Progress,* Bunyan's two other outstanding literary works are *The Holy War* and *The Life and Death of Mr Badman.* Extended extracts from these two books are included here.

The Holy War is a panorama of the battle between Prince Emmanuel and Diabolus for the possession of Mansoul, a 'fair and delicate' town which Shaddai, the first Founder and Builder, made for his own delight.

In *The Life and Death of Mr Badman,* Bunyan depicts the career of an ungodly profligate who deliberately cries, 'Evil be thou my good'. Bunyan wrote this book as a companion volume to *The Pilgrim's Progress,* as he explains in his original preface. Having written about 'the progress of the pilgrim from this life to glory', he went on to elaborate on 'the life and death of the ungodly and of their travel from this world to the next'.

Part II of *The Pilgrim's Progress* includes two well-known poems, still sung as hymns today. Also included in this anthology is an example of what C. H. Spurgeon referred to as 'Master Bunyan's doggerel', some verses on the theme of 'Candles', which present a good example of Bunyan's didactic style in his rhyming verse.

The selection of extracts from Bunyan's sermons opens with one of his prison sermons, *The Holy City,* first published in 1665. It is based on verses from Revelation 21. Bunyan was at heart as much a pastor as an evangelist and this is apparent in his *Advice to Sufferers, or Seasonable*

Counsel, first published in 1684. This is followed by an extract from a sermon first published in 1685 but rarely seen today, entitled *The Pharisee and the Publican*. There follows part of one of Bunyan's most forceful sermons, *Come and Welcome Jesus Christ*, also first published in 1685.

The Water of Life was written in Bunyan's last year, 1688; it is an endearing sermon about the grace and the spirit of the gospel. Part of Bunyan's last sermon, preached on 9 August, twelve days before his death, is included, as are a few extracts from a small collection of Bunyan's aphorisms, collected by George Cockayn and published after Bunyan's death in a book called *Mr John Bunyan's Dying Sayings*.

In the last week of Bunyan's life, before 'a violent fever' overtook him, he corrected proofs of *The Acceptable Sacrifice*. The present anthology concludes with extracts from this exposition of Psalm 51:17, on the virtues of a broken heart and the benefits of a contrite spirit.

Notes

1 John Brown, *John Bunyan, his life, times and work*. Isbister, 1885, p. 482.
2 David Marshall, *An Introduction to the Life and Works of John Bunyan*. Bishopgate Press, 1989, p. 7.
3 Brown, p. 89.
4 Brown, p. 189.
5 John Foxe, *The Book of Martyrs*, revised, with notes and an appendix by William Bramley-Moore. Cassell, Petter, and Galpin, 1895.
6 H. A. Taine, *History of English Literature*, i, p. 398.

1

Grace Abounding

[The original half-title page read: *Grace Abounding to the chief of Sinners: or, A Brief and Faithful Relation of the exceeding mercy of God in Christ, to his poor servant John Bunyan. Wherein is particularly shewed, the manner of his conversion, his fight and trouble for sin, his dreadful temptations, also how he despaired of God's mercy, and how the Lord at length through Christ did deliver him from all the guilt and terror that lay upon him.*

'Come and hear, all ye that fear God; and I will declare what he hath done for my soul.' Psalm 66:16.]

In this account of the merciful working of God on my soul, it will not be amiss if in the first place I do, in a few words, give you details about my upbringing; so that the goodness of God to me may be clearly seen by the sons of men.

For my descent then, it was, as is well known by many, of a low and inconsiderable generation; my father's house being of that rank that is meanest, and most despised of all the families in the land. Wherefore I have not here, as others, to boast of noble blood, or of a high-born state according to the flesh; though all things considered, I magnify the heavenly majesty, for that by this door he brought me into the world, to take part of the grace and life that is in Christ through the gospel.

But yet notwithstanding the meanness and inconsiderableness of my parents, it pleased God to put it into their heart to place me in a school where I learned to read and write. I also attained, according to the rate of other poor men's children, though to my shame I confess, I did soon lose the little I learned, nearly completely, and that long before the Lord converted my soul.

As for my earthly life, for the time that I was in the world without God, it was indeed according to the course of this world, and the spirit that now works in the children of disobedience (Ephesians 2:2–3). I was delighted to be taken a prisoner by the devil, at his will (2 Timothy 2:26). I was filled with all unrighteousness which worked so strongly in my heart and life that as a child I had few equals both for cursing, swearing, lying and for taking God's name in vain.

I was so settled and rooted in these things that they were second nature to me. Since then, I have soberly considered, that I did so offend the Lord, that even as a child he did hardly frighten, even though I had terrifying dreams and visions. For often, after I had spent this or that day in sin, I was greatly afflicted on my bed, and while asleep had visions of devils and evil spirits, who tried, I thought, to take me away with them, and who I could never be rid of.

Also I should during these years be greatly afflicted and troubled with thoughts about the day of judgment, both night and day, and should tremble at the thoughts of the fearful torments of hell fire. I still feared that it would be my lot to be found among those devils and hellish fiends and tied up with chains of eternal darkness.

These things, I say, when I was but a child, about 9 or 10 years old, did so distress my soul, that in the middle of many childish activities, in the company of my friends, I was often greatly depressed and afflicted in my mind, but I refused to let go of my sins. I often despaired about life and heaven and even wished that there was no hell, or that I had been the Devil, thinking that he was only a torturer.

If necessary I would have preferred to be a torturer than to be on the receiving end of torture.

After a time these terrible dreams left me so I soon forgot about them. My pleasures erased them from my mind. With greater greediness I gave full rein to my lusts and delighted in breaking God's laws. When I came to be married I was the ringleader of my circle of friends and led them into all kinds of vice and ungodliness.

The lusts and fruits of the flesh had taken such a hold on my poor soul that if the miracle of God's grace had not gone before me, I would have both perished at the hand of eternal justice, and have brought utter shame and disgrace upon myself.

At that time the thought of religion was abhorrent to me. I could not accept it for myself, or allow others to accept it. When I saw some books about Christian piety, it was as if I was in a prison. 'Then I said unto God, depart from me, for I desire not the knowledge of thy ways' (Job 21:14–15). I was now void of all good understanding. Heaven and hell were far from my mind, as was salvation and damnation. 'O Lord, thou knowest my life, and my ways were not hid from thee.'

I clearly remember that although I found it easy to sin and take delight in the most evil of my friends, yet even then, if I ever saw those who professed to be good, do wicked things, it would make my spirit tremble. I once heard a religious man swear and this affected me so much that it made my heart ache.

But God did not completely leave me, but followed me still, not now with convictions, but judgments, yet such as were mixed with mercy. For I once fell into a creek and barely escaped being drowned. On another occasion I fell out of a boat into the Beford River [that is, the river Ouse] but was again mercifully preserved. I was once in a field, with one of my friends, and an adder happened to come along our path. I had a stick in my hand and I struck on its back, stunned it, forced its mouth open with my stick and pulled out its sting from inside its mouth. If God had not been merciful to me here I could have been killed.

I also have reason to be grateful to God during the time that I was a soldier. I had been told to go to besiege a certain place. But, as I was not ready to go, somebody else went in my place. When they came to besiege the place he was on guard duty and was shot through the head by a musket bullet and killed.

Here, as I said, were judgments and mercy, but neither of them woke up my soul to righteousness, so I continued to sin, grew more and more rebellious against God, and cared less and less about my own salvation.

Soon after this, I got married, and in God's mercy, to a godly wife. We came together as poor as poor can be, and did not have so much as a dish or a spoon between us for our home. But, for her part, she had two books which had been her father's: *The Plain Man's Pathway to Heaven*, by Arthur Dent, and *The Practice of Piety* by Lewis Bayley. We sometimes read these books together and I found in them some things which pleased me, though I still had no conviction. My wife often told me how godly her father had been and how he had reproved vice in his own home and among his neighbours, and that he led a strict and holy life, both in word and deed.

So these books, and my wife, though they did not wake up my heart to my sad sinful state, they did stir up religious thoughts within me. So, because I knew no better, I joined in the religion of the day, and went to church twice a day, along with other people who said and sang devout things. However, I retained my wicked life. But I was so overcome by a superstitious spirit that I loved everything that belonged to church – the high-place, priest, clerk, vestments, the services and everything else. I thought that everything in church was holy, especially the priest and the clerk, because they must have been greatly blessed by God, and were the most important people in God's holy temple, doing his work.

This conceit soon grew so strong that I had only to see a priest, even one who lived a sordid and debauched life, and my spirit would collapse under his, and I would reverence him and cling to him. I supposed that they were God's ministers and could have laid down at their feet and been trampled underfoot by them. Their names, clothes and work intoxicated and bewitched me.

All this time I was unaware about the danger and evil of sin. I was prevented from thinking that sin would damn me, no matter what religion I followed, if I did not find Christ. I never thought about him or even if he ever existed. In this state, men are blind, and wander around wearing themselves out with vanities, because they do not know the way to the city of God (Ecclesiastes 10:15).

But one day, among all the sermons our parson preached, his subject was how to live on the Sabbath day, and the evil of breaking the Sabbath, by working or by playing sports. My conscience was smitten by his sermon, thinking that he directed his words straight at me to show up all my evil ways. I then felt guilt as I never before felt guilt. So I went home burdened in my spirit.

For that moment I was smitten about my previous pleasures. But this did not last and before I had finished eating my mind was eased and my heart returned to its old ways. How happy I was to return to my old ways, and that the fire had been put out, so that I might sin again without being controlled. So, when I had satisfied my nature with food, I tossed the sermon out of my mind and returned to my customary sports with great delight.

On the same day I was in the middle of a game of Cat [a forerunner of cricket] and had just hit the ball with my stick. Then, as I was about to strike the ball for a second time a voice from heaven spoke to my soul, 'Will you leave your sins, and go to heaven? Or will you keep your sins, and go to hell?' This greatly confused me. I left my cat on the ground and looked up to heaven. It was as if the eyes of my understanding had seen the Lord Jesus looking down on me with great displeasure and threatening to punish me for this and for my other ungodly practices.

I had no sooner thought about this than I concluded that I had been a great and grievous sinner, and that it was now too late for me to look for heaven; for Christ would not forgive me, nor pardon my transgressions. As I reflected about this I fell into a pit of depression. I saw that it was too late and so resolved to carry on sinning. I concluded that as I was in a miserable state, I would still be in a miserable state if I ceased to sin, and so could only remain in this miserable state if I continued to sin. I could only be damned, and if I was going to be damned, I might as well be damned for many sins as for a few sins. I stood like this in the middle of the game with everyone looking at me. But I did not tell them anything. I just resolved to carry on with the game.

I continued in this sin for about another month, or more. But one day, as I was standing next to a neighbour's shop window, cursing and swearing like a madman, in my usual way, a woman, sitting inside the house, heard me. Although she was an ungodly wretch herself, she protested that I swore and cursed so badly that I made her tremble. She also told me that I was the ungodliest person she had ever heard swearing in all her life; and that I, by doing this, would ruin all the youth of the town, if they kept my company.

At this reproof I was silenced, and put to secret shame; and that too, I thought, before the God of heaven: wherefore, while I stood there, and hanging down my head, I wished with all my heart that I might be a young child again so that my father could teach me to speak again without all this wicked swearing. For I thought that I am so used to swearing that I could never break the habit.

I do not know how it happened, but from this time forward, I stopped swearing, much to my own amazement. Previously, I had not known how to speak, unless I preceded and followed what I said with an oath, to give it authority. Now I discovered that I could speak better without swearing at all. All this time I did not know Jesus Christ, and I did not stop my sports.

Soon after this I became friends with a poor man, who professed to be religious. I thought, then, that he talks well of the Scriptures and about religious matters. As I admired him, I turned to my Bible and started to read it, especially the historical books. But I could not cope with Paul's letters as I remained ignorant of my corrupt nature and about my need of Jesus Christ to save me.

I engaged in some outward reformation, both in my speech and in my life and set the ten commandments in my sights as the way to heaven. I tried to keep them, and thought that I managed this pretty well sometimes. When I broke one of the commandments my conscience was hurt and I repented and promised God that I would do better next time. I thought that I pleased God as well as anyone in England.

I continued to be like this for about a year, during which time our neighbours took me to be a very godly person. They were astounded to see such a great change in my life. This was indeed the case, even though I still did not know Christ, or about grace, faith or hope. I now know that I would have been in a fearful state had I died then. Although I spoke as if I was a very religious person I was nothing but a poor painted hypocrite. Yet I loved to talk as if I was truly holy. I did all I did, either to be seen by others, or to be well spoken of by them.

You should know that before this time I had taken much delight in bell-ringing, but my tender conscience told me that this was a vain practice and that I should stop. So I stopped bell-ringing, but I still went to the Steeple house and watched. Then I thought it was wrong to watch others as they rang the bells, but I continued to look and watch them. Then, I wondered what would happen if one of the bells fell. I decided to stand under the main beam on which the bells swung. Then I realised that if a bell fell it would first hit the wall and then bounce on to me and kill me. After this I did not go to watch the bell-ringers any more.

I also went in for dancing and it took me a whole year before I managed to give it up. All this time, when I thought that I kept this or that commandment, I had great peace in my conscience, and thought to myself, that God cannot but be pleased with me, as I reckoned than no one in England could please God better than I.

But, poor wretch as I was, I was all this while ignorant of Jesus Christ, and going about to establish my own right-eousness, and would have perished, had not God merci-fully shown me more of my natural state.

One day, in God's providence, I was walking through one of the streets of Bedford. I came across three or four poor women sitting at a door in the sun, talking about the things of God. I wanted to hear what they were saying so I went up to them for I was now good at having conversa-tions about religion myself. Now I heard, but did not understand what I heard. For what they said was way beyond my understanding. They spoke of new birth, the work of God in their hearts, and how they were convinced about their natural miserable state. They talked about how God had visited their souls with his love in the Lord Jesus, and with what words and promises they had been refreshed, comforted, and supported against the devil's temptations. Moreover, they spoke about particular satanic suggestions and temptations. They told each other how they had been afflicted and how they had been borne up under his assaults. They also spoke about their own wretchedness of heart, of their unbelief, and about their own righteousness as filthy, and insufficient to do them any good.

I thought they spoke as joy made them speak. They spoke most pleasantly, using scriptural language, and with an appearance of grace in everything that they said. They made me think that I had discovered another world, as if they were people who lived alone, and were not to be thought of as neighbours (Numbers 23:9).

This made my own heart shake and I began to mistrust my own thoughts about religion and salvation. The new birth never entered into my thinking, and I did not know the comfort of the Word and God's promises, nor did I know the deceitfulness and treachery of my own wicked heart. As far as secret thoughts were concerned, I took no notice of them. I just did not understand what Satan's temptations were, let alone how they were to be resisted.

I left them after I had thought about what they had said and went on my way again. But their conversation went with me, and my heart stayed with them, for I was greatly affected by their words. I was convinced that I wanted the true tokens of a truly godly life and I saw that they had found such a happy and blessed state. So I made it my business to go, again and again, to be with these poor people, for I could not stay away. The more I went among them, the more I questioned my own condition. Soon, I discovered two things within myself, which made me often marvel (especially when I thought what a blind, ignorant, sordid and ungodly wretch I had been just before this). First, I experienced a very great softness and tenderness of heart, which made me fall under the conviction of what they asserted from the Scriptures. Second, my mind kept on meditating about them, and about all the other good things I had ever thought about or read about.

My mind was so influenced by these things that it lay like a leech on a vein, crying out 'Give, give' (Proverbs 30:15). Yes, my mind was fixed in this way on the things about the kingdom of God and eternity, as much as it knew how, even though, as God knows, this was very little. Nevertheless, my mind was fixed on heaven so that no pleasures could distract me back to this earth.

There is one thing I should not forget to mention. There was a young man in our town to whom my heart was bound more than to anyone else. But because he was a most wicked person, cursing, swearing, and whoring, I shook him off and left his company. About three months after I had left him I met him in a certain lane and asked him how he was. After he had sworn in his mad way, he said he was well. 'But, Harry,' I said, 'why do you swear and curse in this way? What will happen to you if you die in this condition?' He answered me in a great rage, 'What would the devil do for company if I were not as I am?'

In those days the Bible became very precious to me. I now began to look at the Bible with new eyes, and read it as I had never done before. Paul's letters were particularly sweet and pleasant to me. I never stopped reading the Bible and meditating on what it said. I cried to God trying to discover the truth and the way to heaven and to glory.

As I carried on reading I came to the passage: 'To one is given by the Spirit the word of wisdom; to another the word of knowledge by the same Spirit, and to another faith' from 1 Corinthians chapter 12. Since then I have realised that the Holy Spirit is referred to in this passage, who does extraordinary and special things. But at the time I was convinced that I did want ordinary things, the understanding and wisdom which other Christians possessed. As I thought about these words I did not know what to do. I was especially puzzled by the word 'faith', and I did not know if I had faith or not. I feared that not having this faith excluded me from all the blessings that other good people received from God. However, I was loath to conclude that I had no faith in my soul. For if I did that, I thought that I would have to count myself a complete castaway.

'No,' I said to myself, 'while I am convinced that I am an ignorant person, and that I do desire those blessed gifts of knowledge and understanding that other people possess, yet I venture to conclude that I am not completely faithless, even though I do not know what faith is.' For it was shown me, and that too (as I have since realised) by Satan, that the people who conclude that they are in a faithless state, have neither rest nor quiet for their souls. I was determined not to fall into despair.

So this suggestion made me frightened to look at my lack of faith. But God would not allow me to undo and destroy my soul, but continually, against my blind and sad condition, did create within me such suppositions that I could not rest until I knew for certain whether I had faith or not. The thought was always running through my mind, 'What if you do lack faith? How can you tell if you have faith?' Besides this, I knew for certain that if I did not possess faith that I would perish for ever.

While I was considering this matter the Tempter came to me and deluded me. He said, 'There is no way you can know if you have faith, unless you try to perform a miracle.' The Tempter backed up this suggestion with Bible verses that seemed to support what he said. One day, as I was between Elstow and Bedford, I was strongly tempted to see if I had any faith by trying to perform a miracle. This was the miracle I attempted. I must say to the puddles that were on the bridle path, 'Be dry'; and say to the dry ground, 'Become puddles'. I was on the verge of doing this when the following thought came to mind, 'Go under that nearby hedge, and pray there, so that God will make you able to perform the miracle.' I had concluded that I must pray, but then I thought, 'If I do pray and nothing happens then I can be certain that I have no faith, but am a castaway and lost.' So I decided that in case this proved to be true I would not attempt the miracle.

So I continued to be in a great quandary. I thought: If only people with faith can do such wonderful things, I must be without faith and am not likely ever to possess it. Thus I was tossed between the devil and my own ignorance. I was so perplexed about this that I often did not know what to do.

As I continued in this great distress I went around bemoaning my sad condition, counting myself worse than a thousand fools for spending so many years in sin. I wished that I had turned to God sooner. I became angry with myself that all I had done was to trifle away my time until my soul and heaven were lost.

When I was gripped by this fear and hardly able to take any further step, at nearly the same place that I had received my earlier encouragement, these words came to mind, 'Compel them to come in, that my house may be filled, and yet there is room' (Luke 14:22–23). These words, and especially the words, 'and yet there is room', were sweet words to me. For I reckoned that through them I saw that there was a place in heaven for me. I also thought that when the Lord Jesus spoke these words, he was thinking of me, and that he knew that the time would come when I was afflicted with fear, thinking that there was no place left for me in his heart. So he left these words on record which he had previously uttered that I might find help through them with this vile temptation. I truly believed this.

I continued in the light and encouragement of this word for quite a while. The comfort increased when I thought that the Lord Jesus should have thought about me so long ago, and that he should have deliberately have spoken them for my sake. I was certain that he spoke them so that I would derive encouragement from them.

After this I found through reading the word, that those who will be glorified with Christ in another world 'must be called by him here'. They must be called to take part in his word and righteousness, in the comforts and the firstfruits of the Spirit, and to a special interest in all the heavenly things which come to the soul for that rest and house of glory in heaven above.

So, once again, I did not know what to do, as I feared that I had not been called. I thought: What if I have not been called? What then can do me good? Only those who are effectively called inherit the kingdom of heaven. Oh how I now loved those words which spoke about a 'Christian calling' – as when the Lord said to one person, 'Follow me'; and to another person, 'Come after me'. I was convinced that he would say such words to me also. Then I would gladly run after him.

I cannot now express with what longings my soul cried to Christ to call me. For some time I continued like this, longing to be converted by Christ. I realised that the converted state was so glorious that I could not rest content until I shared in it. Gold! If it could have been bought with gold, what I would have given for it! If I possessed the whole world, I would have given it ten thousand times over, for this, so that my soul might live in a converted state.

Everyone who I thought was converted was now beautiful in my eyes. They shone. They walked like people who carried the broad seal of heaven about them. I realised that their lot had fallen in pleasant places and that they had goodly heritage (Psalm 16). But what made me feel ill, was that Christ 'went up into a mountain, and called to him whom he would' (Mark 3:13).

This scripture made me faint and fear, yet it kindled fire in my soul. What made me fear was that Christ might not like me, for he called 'whom he would'. But what glory came to my condition, and engaged my heart, that I could seldom read about any people who Christ did call, without wishing: If only I had been in their clothes. If only I had been born Peter. Would that I had been born John. If only I had been there and heard him calling them, how I would have cried, 'O Lord, call me also!' But I feared that he would not call me.

Truly the Lord let me continue like this for many months and showed me nothing. He did not tell me that I was about to be called or that I would be called hereafter. But, at last, after I had spent a great deal of time like this, and after many groans to God asking that I might take part in the holy, heavenly calling, this word came to me, 'I will cleanse their blood that I have not cleansed: for the Lord dwelleth in Zion' (Joel 3:21). I believed that these words were sent to me to encourage me to continue waiting for God. They indicated to me that, if I was not already at the present time, the time would come when I would be converted to Christ.

About this time I began to talk about my state of mind to those poor people in Bedford. When they heard about this they told Mr Gifford [minister of the Independent congregation at Beford] about me. Mr Gifford himself took the trouble to talk with me and was willing to listen to everything that I said. He invited me to his house, where I heard him talk with other people of God's dealings with the soul. This gave me even greater conviction about the inner wretchedness of my wicked heart, for as yet I knew nothing about that matter. This was now revealed to me and I began to see the evil of wickedness as I had never seen it before. I now discovered that evil desires were powerfully at work in me, through my wicked thoughts. I saw in a way that I had never seen before. My desire for heaven and life began to wilt. I found that where previously my soul had been full of longings for God, now my heart began to hanker after every foolish vanity. Yes, my heart would not be moved to seek after what was good. It began to be careless, both about my soul and about heaven. My mind acted like clogs: it held me back, as clogs are used to prevent hawks from flying when they are being trained.

While I was thus afflicted about the fears of my own damnation two things gave me reason to think. First, when I saw old people hunting after the things of this life. Second, when I came across those who professed to believe, but were in much distress as a result of losing a husband, wife or child. Lord, I thought, what a to-do about such little things and how some people run after worldly things. They expend so much energy over, and shed so many tears over, this present life. How much I need to be cried over and prayed for as my soul is in danger of damnation. If only my soul was in a good condition and if only I was certain about this. How rich should

I esteem myself, though blest but with bread and water: I should count those but small afflictions, and should bear them as little burdens. A wounded spirit who can bear?

And though I was thus troubled and tossed and afflicted with the sight and terror of my own wickedness, yet I was afraid to let this sight leave my mind. For I found that unless a guilty conscience was taken right away, that is, by the blood of Christ, a man grew rather worse for the loss of his troubled mind, not better. So if my guilt pressed down on me then I cried that the blood of Christ should remove it. And if it was going off without it (for the sense of sin would be sometimes as if it would die,) then I would also strive to bring it on my heart again, by bringing the punishment for sin in hell-fire to my spirit. Then I cried, 'Lord, let it not go off my heart but by the right way, by the blood of Christ, and by the application of your mercy show him to my soul'. For one scripture which pressed on my soul at this time said, 'Without shedding of blood there is no remission' (Hebrews 9:22). What made me even more afraid of this was that I had seen some people who, even though they had a wounded conscience, would cry and pray. They were, however, seeking to alleviate their present troubles, rather than pardon for their sins. All they cared about was ridding themselves of their guilt. Because their guilt was taken away from them in the wrong way, they enjoyed no sanctification, but they became harder and blinder and more wicked than ever. This made me afraid, and made me cry to God even more, that it would not be like this with me.

I remember that one day, as I was travelling into the country and musing on the wickedness and blasphemy of my heart, and considering the enmity that was in me towards God, the following scripture came to my mind, 'He hath made peace by the blood of his cross' (Colossians 1:20). By this I was made to see both again, and again, and again, that day, that God and my soul were friends by this blood; yes, I saw that the justice of God and my sinful soul, could embrace and kiss each other through this blood. This was a good day to me, I hope I shall not forget it.

At another time, as I sat by the fire in my house, and musing on my wretchedness, the Lord made that also a precious word to me, 'For as much then as the children are partakers of flesh and blood, he also himself likewise took part of the same, that through death he might destroy him that had the power of death, that is the devil: and deliver those who through the fear of death were all their lifetime subject to bondage' (Hebrews 2:14–15). I thought that the glory of these words was then so weighty on me, that I was both once and twice ready to faint as I sat, yet not with grief and trouble, but with solid joy and peace.

At this time also I sat under the ministry of holy Mr Gifford, whose teaching, by God's grace, helped me greatly to become stable. This man made it his business to deliver God's people from all those false and unsound ideas that we by nature take into our souls. He pressed us to take special heed that we take no truth on trust from any person, but cry mightily to God, that he would convince us of its reality, and set us down in it, by his own Spirit in the holy Word. For, he said, if you do otherwise, when strong temptations come on you, if you have not received evidence from heaven, you will lack the help and strength to resist, which you previously thought you possessed.

This was as seasonable to my soul, as the former and latter rain in their season. For I had found, and that by sad experience, the truth of his words. For I had felt, 'no man can say,' especially when tempted by the devil, 'that Jesus Christ is Lord, but by the holy Ghost.' Wherefore I found my soul, through grace, very ready to drink in this teaching, and to pray to God that in nothing that belonged to God's glory and to my own eternal happiness, he would allow me to be without the confirmation which comes from heaven. For now I saw clearly that there was an exceeding difference between the notions of flesh and blood, and the revelations of God in heaven; also a great difference between that faith that is false, and according to man's wisdom, and that which comes through a man being born of God (Matthew 16:15–16; 1 John 5:1).

But, oh, now, how was my soul led from truth to truth by God, even from the birth and cradle of the Son of God, to his ascension and second coming from heaven to judge the world. Truly, I then found upon this account the great God was very good to me, for I remembered that there was not anything that I then cried to God about to make known and reveal to be which he did not so do. I mean not one part of the gospel of the Lord Jesus, but I was orderly led into it; me thought I saw with great evidence, from the testimony of the four evangelists, the wonderful work of God in giving Jesus Christ to save us, from his conception and birth, even to his second coming to judgment. It was as if I had seen him born, as if I had seen him grow up, as if I had seen him walk through this world, from the cradle to the cross. I also saw how he gently gave himself to be hanged and nailed on the cross for my sins and wicked deeds. Also, as I was musing on this, the following words fell on my spirit, 'He was ordained for the slaughter' (1 Peter 1:19–20).

God dealt with me in the following way. First, he allowed me to be afflicted with temptation about believing him, and then he would reveal the truth about himself. Sometimes I lay under the great weight of the guilt of sin, which crushed me to the ground. Then the Lord would show me Christ's death, and in this way sprinkle my conscience with his blood. Then I discovered, even before I became fully aware of it, that in that conscience where anger and law had just reigned, there now abided peace and love of God through Christ.

But before I had got far out of these my temptations, I did greatly long to see some ancient godly man's experience, who had written some hundred years before I was born. God, in whose hands are all our days and ways, did put into my hand, one day, a book by Martin Luther, his

commentary on Paul's letter to the Galatians. It was such
an old copy that it was about to fall apart, if it was turned
over. I was very pleased to have such an old book. I soon
found that my own condition was the same as his experience, which he handled in detail and profoundly. It was as
if his book had been written out of my heart. This made
me marvel. Then I thought: This man could not know
anything about the state of Christians now, but must be
speaking about the experience of former days.

Besides, he does most gravely also in that book discuss
the arrival of temptations, namely, blasphemy, despera-
tion, and the like, showing that the law of Moses, as well as
the devil, death, and hell, has a very great hand there. This
was very strange to me, to start with. But as I considered
and watched, I found it to be true. I do prefer this book of
Mr Luther on Galatians, apart from the Holy Bible, before
all the books that I had ever seen, as most fit for a
wounded conscience.

And now I found, I thought, that I loved Christ dearly.
I believed that my soul clung to him, and that my affections clung to him. I felt love towards him as hot as fire.
And now, as Job said, I thought I should die in my nest;
but I did quickly find that my great love was but little, and
that I, who had, as I thought, such burning love towards
Jesus Christ, could let him go again for a trifle. God knows
how to abase us. He can also hide pride from a man. Soon
after this my love was put to the test.

The Tempter came on me again with more grievous and
dreadful temptations than before. I was tempted to separate from this most blessed Christ. I was tempted to
exchange him for the things of this life – for anything.
This temptation lay on me for about a year, and stayed so
closely to me that I was hardly rid of it for one day in a
month, or even for one hour in many days, unless I was
asleep.

One morning, as I lay on my bed, I was, as at other
times, most fiercely assaulted with this temptation, to

'separate and part from Christ'. The wicked suggestion continually ran through my mind, 'Sell him, sell him, sell him, sell him.' My mind answered, as at other times, 'No, no, not for thousands, thousands, thousands.' This happened about twenty times. But at last, after much striving, even until I was almost out of breath, I felt this thought pass through my heart, 'Let him go if he will!' I thought that I felt my heart freely consent to this. Oh, the diligence of Satan! Oh, how desperate man's heart is!

Now was the battle won, and I fell down, like a bird that is shot from the top of a tree, into great guilt and fearful despair. I climbed out of bed and went moping into the field. I had, as God knows, a heart as heavy as any mortal can bear. For about two hours I was like a man bereft of life, beyond all hope of recovery and destined for eternal punishment.

Then the following scripture gripped my soul, 'O profane person, as Esau, who for one morsel of meat sold his birthright; for you know how that afterwards when he would have inherited the blessing, he was rejected, for he found no place for repentance, though he sought it carefully with tears' (Hebrews 12:16–17).

Now I was like a bound person and I felt myself locked into future judgment. For the next two years I experienced nothing except damnation and the expectation of damnation. To my soul, these words were like chains of brass on my legs. These words continually rang in my ears for several months. But about ten or eleven o'clock one day, as I was walking near a hedge, full of sorrow and guilt, as God knows, and feeling sorry for myself, suddenly this sentence came to me like a thunderbolt: 'The blood of Christ remits all guilt.' At this I made a stand in my spirit. With this, this word gripped me, 'The blood of Jesus Christ his Son cleanseth us from all sin' (1 John 1:7).

Now I began to experience peace in my soul. I thought that I saw the Tempter slink away from me, as if he was ashamed about what he had done. At the same time my sin, and the blood of Christ appeared before me. My sin, when compared with Christ's blood, was little more than this little stone in front of me was to the whole field that I could see. This gave me great encouragement for about two to three hours. During this time I also thought I saw by faith the Son of God suffering for my sins. But because I did not remain in this frame of mind, I sank in my spirit under my great weight of sin again.

I now found it hard work to pray to God, because despair was swallowing me up. I thought that I was in the middle of a violent storm that was driving me away from God. When I cried to God for mercy, these thoughts always came into my mind, ''Tis too late; I am lost. God has let me fall, not for my correction, but for my condemnation. My sin is unpardonable.'

About this time I came across the terrible story of that miserable mortal Francis Spira. [In the book *A Relation of the Fearful Estate of Francis Spira, in the year 1548* Spira shows a spiritual despair which was believed to be a sign that he had been presdestined to damnation.] This book troubled my spirit like salt that is rubbed into a wound. Every sentence of that book, every groan he uttered, as well as all his prayers, tears, gnashing of teeth, wringing of hands and pining of spirit under God's mighty hand, were like knives and daggers ripping through my soul. The sentence that especially frightened me was, 'Man knows the beginning of sin, but who knows the end of it?' Then the sentence that I had thought about earlier concluded the matter: 'for you know how that afterwards when he would have inherited the blessing, he was rejected, for he found no place for repentance, though he sought it carefully with tears.'

Then I was struck with a very great trembling. This sometimes meant that for whole days my mind as well as my body would shake and totter under the sense of God's dreadful judgment, which falls on those who have committed the unforgivable sin. My stomach felt as if it was on fire because of my fear. Sometimes I felt as if my breastbone was going to burst asunder. Then I thought about Judas, 'who, by his falling headlong, burst asunder, and all his bowels gushed out' (Acts 1).

This one consideration would always kill my heart, 'My sin was point-blank against my Saviour,' and that I had in my heart said of him, 'Let him go if he will'. Oh, I thought, this sin was bigger than the sins of a country, or a kingdom, or of the whole world. No other sin could compare with mine.

Now I should have found that my mind fled from God, as from the face of a dreadful judge, but my torment was that I could not escape from his hand. 'It is a fearful thing to fall into the hands of the living God' (Hebrews 10). But blessed be his grace, that scripture, in these flying fits would call as running after me, 'I have blotted out as a thick cloud thy transgressions, and as a cloud thy sins: Return unto me, for I have redeemed thee' (Isaiah 44:22). This, I say, would come to my mind, as I was fleeing from God's face; for I did flee from his face, that is, my mind and spirit fled before him; then the text cried, 'Return unto me, for I have redeemed thee.' This would make me stop, and, as it were, to look over my shoulder, to see if I could detect God's grace following me with a pardon in his hand. But as soon as I did that everything became dark all around me on account of the sentence, 'for you know how that afterwards when he would have inherited the blessing, he was rejected, for he found no place for repentance, though he sought it carefully with tears.' So I could not return but fled, though sometimes it cried 'Return, return.' But I was afraid to return, in case this was not from God, for those other words were still ringing in my ears, 'for you know how that afterwards when he would have inherited the blessing, he was rejected, for he found no place for repentance, though he sought it carefully with tears.'

I was once walking to and fro in a shop that belonged to

a good man, bewailing my sad and doleful state. I afflicted myself with self-abhorrence, lamenting that I should have committed such a great sin, fearing that it could never be forgiven. All the time I also prayed in my heart that if this sin of mine was different from the sin against the Holy Spirit, that the Lord would show me. I was just about to sink with fear under the weight of this thought. Suddenly, it sounded as the wind had blown strongly against the window. The noise seemed very pleasant, and it appeared to say, 'Didst ever refuse to be justified by the blood of Christ?' My whole life flashed before my eyes in a second, so I could see that I had never refused Christ on purpose. So my heart answered in a groan, 'No'. Then the words came powerfully over me, 'See that ye refuse not him that speaketh' (Hebrews 12:25).

This gripped my spirit in a strange way. It brought light with it. It silenced all those tumultuous thoughts, which blew like hell-hounds, in my heart. It also showed me that Jesus Christ had yet a work of grace and mercy for me. It showed me, that he had not, as I had feared, quite forsaken and thrown off my soul. Yes, this was a kind of rebuke for my tendency to despair. It reminded me that despite my terrible sins I must receive my salvation from the Son of God. I did not understand this strange dispensation. I did not know where it came from or where it was going to. After twenty years I have not been able to make up my mind about it. 'I thought then what here I should be loath to speak.' But truly by that sudden rushing wind, it was as if an angel had come on me. But I will leave it and the greeting until the day of judgment. I will only say this about it: it produced a great calm in my soul and it gave me grounds for hope. It showed me, I thought, what the unpardonable sin was. It showed me that my soul was going to be blessed and would be privileged to flee to Jesus Christ for mercy. But I still do not know what to say about this dispensation, which is the reason why I did not speak about it at first in the book. I will leave men of sound judgment to think about it. I do not fix my hopes of salvation on it, but on the Lord Jesus and his promise. But, as I am revealing my hidden life, I thought it might be expedient to share it with you, even though I do not understand the experience myself. This experience lasted for about three or four days before I began to fall into despair again.

My life of doubt stood before me and I did not know which way to go. All I knew was that my soul desired to throw itself down at the foot of grace through prayer and supplication. But, it was so hard for me now to show my face and pray to this Christ for mercy, against whom I had so vilely sinned. I repeat, it was hard work to try to look him in the face against whom I had so vilely sinned. Indeed, I have found it just as difficult to come to God in prayer, after I have backslid from him, as to do anything else. How shameful I now felt, especially when I thought: I am now going to pray to him for mercy that I had taken so lightly just the moment before. Yes, I was ashamed, even confounded, because I had committed this villainy. I realised that there was only one thing that I could do. I must go to Christ, and humble myself before him, and beg him, through his wonderful mercy, to show me pity, and have mercy on my wretched sinful soul.

But when the Tempter saw this, he strongly advised me that I should not pray to God. He told me that prayer was no use in my case, and that it would do me no good because I had rejected the Mediator, through whom all acceptable prayers to the Father came, and without whom no prayer could enter his presence. So to pray now would only be to add sin to sin. 'Yes,' explained the Tempter, 'to pray now, seeing that God has thrown you aside, will only increase his anger against you.'

I now found that the most liberating and gracious words in the Gospels were of great torment to me. Yes, nothing afflicted me so much as the thought of Jesus Christ. The remembrance of a Saviour, whom I had rejected, brought to my mind both the villainy of my sin and my great loss.

Nothing hurt my conscience as much as this. Every time I thought of the Lord Jesus, of his grace, love, goodness, kindness, gentleness, meekness, death, blood, promises and blessed exhortations, comforts and consolations, it went through my soul like a sword. For the following thoughts about the Lord Jesus stayed in my heart: 'Yes, this is the Jesus, the loving Saviour, the Son of God, whom you have parted with, whom you slighted, despised, and abused. This is the only Saviour, the only Redeemer, the only one who could so love sinners and wash them from their sins in his own most precious blood. But you have no part or lot in this Jesus, you have put him away from you, you have said in your heart, "Let him go if he will". Now, therefore, you are severed from him; you have severed yourself from him. Behold, then, his goodness, but you yourself do not take part in it.'

Thus was I always sinking, whatever I thought or did. So one day I walked to a neighbouring town, and sat down on a seat in the street, and fell into a very deep pause about the most fearful state my sin had brought me to; and, after long musing, I lifted up my head, but I thought that I saw the light shining as if the sun was giving its light grudgingly. It looked as if the very stones in the street, and the tiles on the houses, were lining up against me and had united to banish me from this world. They rejected me as one who was unfit to live with them, or to enjoy their benefits, because I had sinned against the Saviour.

I then broke out of the bitterness of my soul, saying to myself, with a great sigh, 'How can God comfort such a wretch as me?' No sooner had I said this, but a voice, like an echo to my question, replied, 'This sin is not unto death'. I became like a person who had been raised out of the grave, and cried out again, 'Lord, how could you find out such a word as this?' For I was filled with wonder at the appropriateness and unexpectedness of the sentence. The fitness of the word, the rightness of the timing of it: the power, and sweetness, and light, and glory that came with it also, was marvellous for me to find. For a time, I was no longer doubting about the things that had made me doubt so much in the past. Previously, my fears had been that my sin was unpardonable, so that I had no right to pray or repent. And even if I did pray or repent it would do me no good. But now I thought that if this sin is not to death, then it is pardonable. So from this I am encouraged to come to God through Christ for mercy, to consider the promise of forgiveness, like a person standing with arms wide open waiting to receive me and other people. My mind was greatly eased with these thoughts, that my sin was pardonable, and that it was not the sin unto death (1 John 5:16–17). Only those who know about my troubles, or those who have experienced these things for themselves, can know what a relief came to my soul as I thought about this. It was a release for me, from my previous chains, and a shelter from my previous storm. I now seemed to stand on the same ground as other sinners and to have as much right to the word and to prayer as they did.

Now, as I say, I was hopeful that my sin was not unpardonable, and that there might be hope for me to receive forgiveness. But O how Satan did lay about me, to bring me down again! But he could not succeed, either then or for the most part of the next day. For this sentence stood like a mill-post at my back. Yet towards the next evening, I felt this word begin to leave me, and to withdraw its support from me. I returned to my old fears again, but most reluctantly, as I fear the sorrow of despair. My faith could no longer keep this word.

But the following evening, as I was gripped by these fears, I went to seek the Lord. As I prayed, I cried, and my soul cried to him with these words, crying aloud strongly: 'O Lord, I beseech thee show me that thou hast loved me with an everlasting love' (Jeremiah 31:3). No sooner had I said this than the sweetness returned to me. It came with this echo, 'I have loved thee with an everlasting love'. Now

I went to bed at peace and when I woke up in the morning this word was till fresh on my soul and I believed it.

However, the Tempter did not leave me. He tried to upset my peace as many as a hundred times a day. Oh the fights and conflicts that I had to meet. Yet God bore me up and kept my heart concentrating on this word which had for several days filled me with comfort and hope of pardon. For thus it was made out to me: 'I loved thee whilst thou wast committing this sin, I loved thee before, I love thee still, and I will love thee for ever.'

My heart now began to ache, fearing that I might be disappointed in the end. So I began to examine my former comfort and to consider whether a person who had sinned as I had might with confidence trust God's faithfulness as spoken of in the words that had comforted me so much. Now, however, this saying came to my mind, 'For it is impossible for those who were once enlightened and have tasted of the heavenly gift, and were made partakers of the Holy Ghost, and have tasted the good word of God, and the powers of the world to come; if they shall fall away, to renew them again unto repentance' (Hebrews 6). 'For if we sin wilfully after we have received the knowledge of the truth, there remains no more sacrifice for sin, but a certain fearful looking for of judgment and fiery indignation, which shall devour the adversaries' (Hebrews 10). 'Even as Esau, who for one morsel of meat sold his birthright; for ye know how that afterwards, when he would have inherited the blessing, he was rejected; for he found no place of repentance, though he sought it carefully with tears' (Hebrews 12).

Now the word of the gospel was forced from my soul so that I found no promise or encouragement in the Bible. I was now afflicted by the saying, 'Rejoice not, O Israel, for joy, as other people' (Hosea 9:1). I saw that there was indeed reason for other people who held on to Jesus to rejoice, but as far as I was concerned, I had cut myself off through my transgressions, and left myself no foothold or handhold among the props in the precious Word of Life.

But one morning when I was again at prayer and trembling under the fear that no word of God could help me, part of a sentence darted into my mind, 'My grace is sufficient'. At this I thought there might be some hope. But how good it is that God sends his word! For about a fortnight before, I was looking at this very place, and then I thought it could not come near my soul with comfort, and threw down my book in a rage. Then I thought it was not large enough for me, no, not large enough. But now it was as if it had arms of grace so wide, that it could not only enclose me, but many other people as well.

I was sustained by these words, yet not without exceeding conflicts, for the next seven to eight weeks. My peace would come and go up to twenty times a day: comfort now, and trouble presently; peace now, and before I could go a furlong, as full of fear and guilt as ever a heart could hold. This was not just now and then, but throughout the seven weeks. For the sufficiency of grace and Esau's parting with his birthright were like a pair of scales in my mind; sometimes one would be uppermost, at another time the other would be uppermost, and depending which gained the upper hand I either had peace or trouble.

Therefore I still prayed to God, that he would come in with this Scripture more fully to my heart, so that he would help me to apply the whole sentence, which I was then unable to do. I understood that he gave, but I could go no further than this, for I could only hope that there might be mercy for me and that 'My grace is sufficient'. It answered my first question: that there was hope, but because it left out the words 'for thee' I was not satisfied, and so continued to pray to God. One day, as I was in a meeting with God's people, I was full of sadness and terror as my previous fears now gripped me. I thought that my soul would never progress and that my case was most sad and fearful. Then these words suddenly broke over me in a most powerful way: 'My grace is sufficient for thee, my grace is sufficient for thee, my grace is sufficient for thee.' Yes, it was repeated like this, three times. I found that every word was a powerful word for me – 'my', and 'grace', and 'sufficient', and 'for thee'. They were then, and sometimes still are, bigger than any of the other words.

Thus, for many weeks, I was sometimes comforted, and sometimes tormented. Then I thought that I should see if Peter and Paul and John and all the writers looked on me with scorn and held me up to derision, as if they said to me, 'All our words are true. We have not cut you off, you have cast yourself away. These are the sentences you must take hold of: "It is impossible; there remains no sacrifice for sin" (Hebrews 6). "And it had been better for them not to have known the will of God, than after they have known it, to turn from the holy commandment delivered unto them" (Hebrews 10). "For the Scriptures cannot be broken" (2 Peter 2:21).' I quaked at the apostles. I knew their words were true, and that they must stand for ever.

But one day, as I was passing in the field, and that too with some shade on my conscience, fearing lest yet all was not right, suddenly this sentence fell on my soul, 'Thy righteousness is in heaven'. I thought about this and I saw with the eyes of my soul that Jesus Christ was at God's right hand. He was there as my righteousness, so that wherever I was, or whatever I was doing, God could not say about me, 'He lacks my righteousness,' for that was right in front of him. Moreover, I also saw that it was not my good frame of heart that made my righteousness better, nor yet my bad frame of heart that made my righteousness worse: for my righteousness was Jesus Christ himself, 'the same yesterday, and today, and for ever' (Hebrews 13:8).

Now did my chains fall off my legs indeed, I was loosed from my affliction and irons, my temptations fled away. From that time those dreadful Scriptures from God stopped troubling me. I went home rejoicing, because of the grace and love of God. When I arrived home, I looked to see if I could find the sentence, 'Thy righteousness is in heaven', but could not find such a saying, so my heart began to sink again. The only sentence that came to my mind was, 'He of God is made unto us Wisdom, Righteousness, Sanctification, and Redemption' (1 Corinthians 1:30). Through this word I saw that the other sentence was true.

From this Scripture I saw that the man Jesus Christ, as he is distinct from us as far as his bodily presence is concerned, so he is our righteousness and sanctification before God. Here, therefore, I lived, for some time, very sweetly at peace with God through Christ. I thought: O, Christ! Christ! Nothing but Christ was in front of my eyes. I was only looking at the whole of Christ, not all his benefits – his blood, his burial or his resurrection. In him, these and his other virtues, relations, offices, and operations meet together, as he sits on God's right hand in heaven.

'Twas glorious for me to see his exaltation, and the worth and prevalence of all his benefits, because of what I now understood. Now I could look away from my self to Christ, and should reckon that all those graces of God that were green in me, were like those cracked groats and four half-pennies that rich men carry in their purses, when their gold is in their trunks at home. I saw that my gold was in my trunk at home! In Christ my Lord and Saviour. Now Christ was all; all my wisdom, all my righteousness, all my sanctification, and all my redemption.

Further, the Lord did also lead me into the mystery of union with this Son of God, that I was joined to him, that I was flesh of his flesh, and bone of his bone, and now was that a sweet word to me in Ephesians 5:3. By this also was my faith in him, as my righteousness, the more confirmed to me; for if he and I were one, then his righteousness was mine, his merits mine, his victory also mine. Now could I see myself in heaven and earth at once; in heaven by my Christ, by my head, by my righteousness and life, though on earth by my body or person.

Now I saw Christ Jesus was looked on by God, and should also be looked on by us, in whom all the whole body of his elect are always to be considered and reckoned, that we fulfilled the law by him, rose from the dead by him, won the victory over sin, death, the devil, and hell, by him. When he died, we died; and so of his resurrection: 'thy dead men shall live, together with my dead body shall they arise' he says, (Isaiah 26), and again, 'After two days he will revive us: and the third day we shall live in his sight' (Hosea 6:2), which is now fulfilled as the Son of Man has sat down on the right hand of the majesty in the heavens. Accordingly Ephesians says, 'He hath raised us up together, and made us sit together in heavenly places in Christ Jesus' (Ephesians 2:6).

Ah these blessed considerations and Scriptures, with many similar ones, bathed my eyes in those days, so I have reason to say, 'Praise ye the Lord God in his sanctuary, praise him in the firmament of his power, praise him for his mighty acts, praise him according to his excellent greatness' (Psalm 150:1–2).

Now was my heart full of comfort, for I hope it was sincere. I would not have been without this trial for anything. I am comforted every time I think of it, and I hope that I shall bless God for ever for the teaching that I have had from it. Many more of God's dealings with me I might relate, but these out of the spoils won in battle have I dedicated to maintain the house of God (1 Chronicles 26:27).

Conclusion

Of all the temptations that ever I met with in my life, to question the being of God, and the truth of his gospel, is the worst, and worst to be borne; when this temptation comes, it takes away my girdle from me, and removes the foundations from under me: I have often thought of that word, 'Have your loins girt about with truth'; and of, 'When the foundations are destroyed what can the righteous do?'

Sometimes, after I have sinned, I have looked for sore

chastisement from God's hand, and the very next thing I have received from him is his grace. Sometimes, when I have been comforted, I have called myself a fool for sinking in such a way under troubles. And then, again, when I have been cast down, I thought I was not wise to give way to such comfort. With great power these thoughts have come upon me.

I have wondered much at this one thing, that though God does visit my soul with never so blessed a discovery of himself, yet I have found again, that such hours have attended me afterwards, that I have been in my spirit so filled with darkness, that I could not so much as once conceive what that God and that comfort was with which I have been refreshed.

I have sometimes seen more in a line of the Bible than I could well tell how to stand under, and yet at another time the whole Bible has been as dry as a stick for me, or rather, my heart has been so dead and dry to it, that I could not conceive the least dram of refreshment, though I have looked it all over.

Of all tears, they are the best that are made by the blood of Christ. Of all joy, that is the sweetest that is mixed with mourning over Christ. Oh 'tis a godly thing to be on our knees, with Christ in our arms, before God. I hope I know something of these things.

I find to this day seven abominations in my heart.

1. Inclinings to unbelief.

2. Suddenly to forget the love and mercy that Christ manifests.

3. A leaning to the words of the law.

4. Wanderings and coldness in prayer.

5. To forget to watch for what I pray for.

6. Apt to murmur because I have no more, and yet ready to abuse what I have.

7. I can do none of those things which God commands me, but my corruptions will thrust in themselves. When I would do good, evil is present with me.

These things I continually see and feel, and am afflicted and oppressed with. Yet God's wisdom does order them for my good:

1. They make me abhor myself.
2. They keep me from trusting my heart.
3. They convince me of the insufficiency of all inherent righteousness.
4. They show me the necessity of fleeing to Jesus.
5. They press me to pray to God.
6. They show me the need I have to watch and be sober.
7. And provoke me to look to God through Christ to help me, and carry me through this world. Amen.

2

The Pilgrim's Progress (Part I)
from this world to that which is to come

When at the first I took my pen in hand,
Thus for to write, I did not understand
That I at all should make a little book
In such a mode: nay, I had undertook
To make another; which, when almost done,
Before I was aware, I this begun.

And thus it was: I, writing of the way
And race of saints in this our gospel-day,
Fell suddenly into an allegory
About their journey and the way to glory,
In more than twenty things, which I set down:
This done, I twenty more had in my crown;
And they again began to multiply,
Like sparks that from the coals of fire do fly.
Nay then, thought I, if that you breed so fast,
I'll put you by yourselves, lest you at last
Should prove *ad infinitum*, and eat out
The book that I already am about.

Well, so I did; but yet I did not think
To show to all the world my pen and ink

In such a mode; I only thought to make
I knew not what; nor did I undertake
Thereby to please my neighbour; no, not I;
I did it mine own self to gratify.

Neither did I but vacant seasons spend
In this my scribble; nor did I intend
But to divert myself, in doing this,
From worser thoughts, which make me do amiss.

Thus I set pen to paper with delight,
And quickly had my thoughts in black and white,
For having now my method by the end,
Still as I pull'd, it came; and so I penn'd
It down; until at last it came to be,
For length and breadth, the bigness which you see.

Well, when I had thus put my ends together,
I showed them others, that I might see whether
They would condemn them, or them justify;
And some said, Let them live; some, Let them die:
Some said, John, print it; others said, Not so:
Some said, It might do good; others said, No.

Now was I in a strait, and did not see
Which was the best thing to be done by me:
At last I thought, Since you are thus divided,
I print it will; and so the case decided.
For, thought I, some I see would have it done,
Though others in that channel do not run:
To prove, then, who advisèd for the best,
Thus I thought fit to put it to the test.

I further thought, if now I did deny
Those that would have it thus to gratify,
I did not know, but hinder them I might
Of that which would to them be great delight:

For those which were not for its coming forth,
I said to them, *Offend you I am loth*;
Yet, since your brethren pleasèd with it be,
Forbear to judge, till you do further see.

If that you will not read, let it alone;
Some love the meat, some love to pick the bone;
Yea, that I might them better moderate,
I did too with them thus expostulate:

May I not write in such a style as this?
In such a method, too, and yet not miss
My end, thy good? Why may it not be done?
Dark clouds bring waters, when the bright bring none.
Yea, dark or bright, if they their silver drops
Cause to descend, the earth, by yielding crops,
Gives praise to both, and carpeth not at either,
But treasures up the fruit they yield together;
Yea, so commixes both, that in their fruit
None can distinguish this from that; they suit
Her well when hungry; but if she be full,
She spews out both, and makes their blessings null.

You see the ways the fisherman doth take
To catch the fish; what engines doth he make.
Behold! how he engageth all his wits;
Also his snarers, lines, angles, hooks, and nets:
Yet fish there be, that neither hook nor line,
Nor snare, nor net, nor engine, can make thine:
They must be groped for, and be tickled too,
Or they will not be catch'd, whate'er you do.
How does the fowler seek to catch his game?
By divers means, all which one cannot name:
His guns, his nets, his lime-twigs, light, and bell;
He creeps, he goes, he stands; yea, who can tell
Of all his postures? Yet there's none of these
Will make him master of what fowls he please.

Yea, he must pipe and whistle to catch this,
Yet, if he does so, that bird he will miss.

If that a pearl may in a toad's head dwell,
And may be found, too, in an oyster-shell:
If things that promise nothing do contain
What better is than gold, who will disdain,
That have an inkling of it, there to look,
That they may find it? Now, my little book
(Though void of all these paintings that may make
It with this or the other man to take)
Is not without those things that do excel
What do in brave but empty notions dwell.

Well, yet I am not fully satisfied,
That this your book will stand when soundly tried.

Why, what's the matter? *It is dark!* What though?
But it is feigned. What of that, I trow?
Some men, by feignèd words, as dark as mine,
Make truth to spangle, and its rays to shine!
But they want solidness. Speak, man, thy mind!
They drown the weak; metaphors make us blind.

Solidity, indeed, becomes the pen
Of him that writeth things divine to men:
But must I needs want solidness, because
By metaphors I speak? Were not God's laws,
His gospel laws, in olden time held forth
By shadows, types, and metaphors? Yet loth
Will any sober man be to find fault
With them, lest he be found for to assault
The highest Wisdom. No, he rather stoops,
And seeks to find out what by pins and loops,
By Calves, and Sheep; by Heifers, and by Rams;
By Birds and Herbs, and by the blood of Lambs;
God speaketh to him: And happy is he

That finds the light, and grace that in them be.

Be not too forward therefore to conclude,
That I want solidness; that I am rude:
All things solid in shew, not solid be;
All things in parables despise not we,
Lest things most hurtful lightly we receive;
And things that good are, of our souls bereave.

My dark and cloudy words they do but hold
The Truth, as Cabinets enclose the Gold.

The Prophets used much by metaphors
To set forth Truth; Yea, who so considers
Christ, his Apostles too, shall plainly see,
That Truths to this day in such Mantles be.

Am I afraid to say that holy Writ,
Which for its style, and phrase, puts down all wit,
Is every where so full of all these things,
(Dark figures, allegories) yet there springs
From that same Book that lustre, and those rayes
Of light, that turns our darkest nights to days.

Come, let my Carper, to his Life now look,
And find there darker lines, than in my Book
He findeth any. Yea, and let him know,
That in his best things there are worse lines too.

May we but stand before impartial men,
To his poor One, I durst adventure Ten,
That they will take my meaning of these lines
Far better then his lies in Silver Shrines.
Come, Truth, although in Swadling-clouts, I find
Informs the Judgment, rectifies the Mind,
Pleases the Understanding, makes the Will
Submit; the Memory too it doth fill

With what doth our Imagination please;
Likewise, it tends our troubles to appease.

Sound words I know *Timothy* is to use;
And old Wives' Fables he is to refuse,
But yet grave *Paul* him no where doth forbid
The use of parables; in which lay hid
That God, those Pearls, and precious stones that were
Worth digging for; and that with greatest care.

Let me add one word more, O Man of God!
Art thou offended? does thou wish I had
Put forth my matter in another dress,
Or that I had in things been more express?
Three things let me propound, then I submit
To those that are my betters (as is fit).

1. I find not that I am denied the use
Of this my method, so I no abuse
Put on the Words, Things, Readers, or be rude
In handling Figure, or Similitude,
In application; but, all that I may,
Seek the advance of Truth, this or that way:
Denied did I say? Nay, I have leave,
(Example too, and that from them that have
God better pleased by their words or ways,
Then any Man that breatheth nowadays,)
Thus to express my mind, thus to declare
Things unto thee that excellentest are.

2. I find that men (as high as Trees) will write
Dialogue-wise; yet no Man doth them slight
For writing so: Indeed if they abuse
Truth, cursed be they, and the craft they use
To that intent; but yet let Truth be free
To make her Salleys upon Thee, and Me,
Which way it pleases God. For who knows how,

Better than he that taught us first to Plow,
To guide our Mind and Pens for his Design?
And he makes base things usher in Divine.

3. I find that holy Writ in many places,
Hath semblance with this method, where the cases
Doth call for one thing to set forth another:
Use it I may then, and yet nothing smother
Truths golden Beams; Nay, by this method may
Make it cast forth its rayes as light as day.

And now, before I do put up my Pen,
I'll shew the profit of my Book, and then
Commit both thee, and it unto that hand
That pulls the strong down, and makes weak ones stand.

This Book it chaulketh out before thine eyes,
The man that seeks the everlasting Prize:
It shews you whence he comes, whither he goes,
What he leaves undone; also what he does:
It also shews you how he runs, and runs,
Till he unto the Gate of Glory comes.

It shews too, who sets out for life amain,
As if the lasting Crown they would attain:
Here also you may see the reason why
They lose their labour, and like fools do die.

This Book will make a Travailer of thee,
If by its Counsel thou wilt rulèd be;
It will direct thee to the Holy Land,
If thou wilt its directions understand:
Yea, it will make the sloathful, active be;
The blind also, delightful things to see.

Art thou for something rare, and profitable?
Wouldest thou see a Truth within a fable?

Art thou forgetful? Wouldest thou remember
From *New-years-day* to the last of *December*?
Then read my fancies, they will stick like burs,
And may be to the Helpless, comforters.

This book is writ in such a dialect,
As may the minds of listless men affect:
It seems a novelty, and yet contains
Nothing but sound and honest Gospel-strains.

Wouldst thou divert thy self from Melancholly?
Would'st thou be pleasant, yet be far from folly?
Would'st thou read riddles, and their explanation,
Or else be drownded in thy Contemplation?
Dost thou love picking-meat? or would'st thou see
A man i' the clouds, and hear him speak to thee?
Would'st thou be in a Dream, and yet not sleep?
Or would'st thou in a moment laugh and weep?
Wouldest thou lose thy self, and catch no harm?
And find thy self again without a charm?
Would'st read thy self, and read thou know'st not what
And yet know whether thou art blest or not,
By reading the same lines? O then come hither,
And lay my Book, thy Head and Heart together.

The Hollow and the Dreamer

Walking through the wilderness of this world I came upon
a place where there was a hollow (the gaol). There I lay
down to sleep: and as I slept I dreamed a dream. I
dreamed, and look! I saw a man clothed with rags. He
stood with his face away from his own house, a book in his
hand, and a great burden on his back. I looked, and saw
him open the book, and read it. As he read he wept and
trembled. Unable to contain himself, he broke down with a
heart-breaking cry, calling out, 'What shall I do?' (Isa.
64:6; Luke 14:33; Ps. 38:4; Hab. 2:2; Acts 2:37). And in

this state he went home. Here he held himself back for as long as he could so that his wife and children shouldn't see his distress. But he couldn't be silent for long because his trouble grew worse. Finally he unburdened himself to his wife and children. 'My dear wife,' he said, 'and you children of my deepest love, I, your dear friend, feel utterly crushed under a burden too heavy to bear. The worst of it is, I have sure information that this city of ours will be burned with fire from heaven. In this dreadful destruction, both I, and you, my wife, and you my sweet babies, will be miserably destroyed unless we find some way of escape. But as yet I can see none.'

At this his family were very distressed, not because they believed that what he said to them was true, but because they thought that some madness had got into his head. As it was drawing towards night and they hoped that sleep might settle his mind, they hastily got him to bed. But the night was as troublesome to him as the day. And instead of sleeping he spent it in sighs and tears.

When morning came they wanted to know how he was and he told them, 'It's worse and worse'. He also set about talking to them again. But they began to grow hard. They thought that a harsh, surly attitude would drive away this derangement. Sometimes they derided, sometimes they scolded, and sometimes they totally neglected him. As a result he began to withdraw to his own room to pray for and pity them, and also to grieve over his misery. He began to walk by himself in the fields, sometimes reading and sometimes praying. For some days he spent his time in this way.

Now one day he was walking in the fields reading his book as usual, and feeling greatly distressed, when he burst out, as he had done before, with the cry, 'What must I do to be saved?' (Acts 16:30). He looked one way and then the other as if he wanted to run. Yet he stood still and I saw that this was because he couldn't tell which way to run.

Then I saw a man coming to him whose name was Evangelist. He asked, 'Why are you crying?'

'Sir,' he answered, 'I understand from this book I'm holding that I'm condemned to die and after that to face judgment (Heb. 9:27); and I find that I'm not willing to do the first (Job 16:21–22), nor able to do the second' (Ezek. 22.14).

Evangelist then said, 'Why aren't you willing to die, since this life has so many evils?'

The man answered, 'Because I'm afraid that this burden on my back will sink me lower than the grave, and I'll fall into Topheth (Isa. 30:33). And, sir, if I'm unfit to go to prison I'm certainly not fit to go to judgment, and from there to execution. It's the thought of all these things that makes me cry.'

Then Evangelist said, 'If this is your condition, why are you standing still?'

He answered, 'Because I don't know where to go.'

Then Evangelist gave him a parchment in which was written, 'Flee from the coming wrath' (Matt. 3:7).

So the man read it, and looking at Evangelist very carefully he said, 'Where must I flee to?'

Then Evangelist pointed with his finger over a very wide field. 'Do you see that distant wicket-gate?' he asked (Matt. 7:14).

The man said, 'No'.

'Well, do you see that shining light in the distance?' (Ps. 119:105; 2 Pet. 1:19).

'I think I do.'

Then Evangelist said, 'Keep that light in your eye and go straight towards it. Then you'll see the gate. When you knock on it you'll be told what to do.'

So in my dream I saw that the man began to run. But he hadn't run far from his own door when his wife and children saw him and began to cry out to him to return (Luke 14:26). But the man put his fingers in his ears and ran on crying, 'Life! Life! Eternal life!' He didn't look back, but fled towards the middle of the plain (Gen. 19:17).

The neighbours too came out to see the man run. Some mocked (Jer. 20:10) as he ran, others threatened, and some implored him to return. Among all these there were some who resolved to fetch him back by force.

One was named Obstinate and the other Pliable. Now by this time the man was a good distance from them, but they were determined to pursue him, and in a little while they overtook him.

Then the man said, 'Why have you come, friends?'

They said, 'To persuade you to go back with us.'

But he said, 'No! That's impossible. I know you live in the city of Destruction, the place where I was born. Sooner or later you'll die there and you'll sink lower than the grave to a place that burns with fire and sulphur. You're good neighbours, be content to come along with me.'

'What!' said Obstinate, 'and leave our friends? Leave all our comforts behind us!'

'Yes,' said Christian, for that was the man's name, 'because what you're leaving isn't worth half of what I'm seeking to enjoy (2 Cor. 4:18). And if you do go along with me and don't give up, you'll fare as well as I do, for where I'm going there's enough and to spare (Luke 15:17). Come on. Prove it.'

'What are these things, you're leaving all the world for?' asked Obstinate.

'I seek an "inheritance that can never perish, spoil or fade" (1 Pet. 1:4), "it's kept in heaven", safe there, ready to be given at the appointed time to everyone who looks hard for it (Heb. 11:16). Read about it, if you want, in the book.'

'Rubbish!' said Obstinate. 'Get away with your book! Will you go back with us or not?'

'No, not me, because I've put my hand to the plough' (Luke 9:62).

'Right, then. Come on, Pliable, let's turn back and go home without him. We're in the company of one of those crazy-headed jackasses who gets hold of a whim and in the end thinks he's wiser than seven sane men.'

Then Pliable said, 'Don't be so abusive. If what Christian says is true, the things he's seeking are better than ours. I'm inclined to go with my neighbour.'

'What! Even more of a fool!' exclaimed Obstinate. 'Take my advice. Come on back. Who knows where someone so sick in the head will lead you? Show a bit of sense and come back.'

'No, come with me, Pliable,' Christian urged. 'There really are such things for us to possess and many more splendours besides. If you don't believe me, read for yourself here in this book. Its truth is guaranteed by the blood of the one who made it. Look!' (Heb. 9:17–21).

'Well, Obstinate,' said Pliable, 'I'm about to make a decision. I intend to go along with my friend here and cast in my lot with him. But, look here,' he said to Christian, 'do you know the way to this desirable place?'

'A man called Evangelist directed me to hurry on to a little gate just ahead of us,' Christian replied, 'where we'll be given instructions about the way.'

'Come on then,' said Pliable, 'let's get going.'

So they then both went on together.

'And I'll go back to my place,' said Obstinate. 'I'm not keeping company with such deluded maniacs.'

The Slough of Despond

Now in my dream I saw that when Obstinate had gone back Christian and Pliable went on over the plain, talking together.

Christian said, 'Well, Pliable. How're you, friend? I'm glad you decided to go along with me. If Obstinate had felt what I've felt of the powers and terrors of the unseen, he wouldn't have been so quick to turn his back on us.'

'Well then, Christian, as there's no one apart from us to hear, tell me more. What are these things you're on about? How can we enjoy them, and where are we going?'

'I can picture them in my mind, better than describe them with words. But even so, as you do want to know I'll read about them from my book.'

'And do you think that the words of your book are really true?'

'Oh yes, absolutely. Because it was made by the one who doesn't lie' (Titus 1:2).

'Well said! What are these things, Christian?'

'There's an everlasting kingdom to be inherited, and eternal life to be given us, that we may inhabit the kingdom for ever' (Isa. 45:17; John 10:27–9).

'Well said! And what else?'

'There are crowns of glory to be given us and clothes to make us shine like the sun in the firmament of heaven' (2 Tim. 4:8; Rev. 3:4; Matt. 13:43).

'This is splendid! And what else?'

'There will be no more crying nor sorrow, for the owner of the place will wipe every tear from our eyes' (Isa. 25:8; Rev. 7:16–17, 21:4).

'And what sort of company shall we have there?'

'There we'll be with Seraphs and will see Cherubim – creatures that'll dazzle your eyes (Isa. 6:2; 1 Thess. 4:16–17; Rev. 5:11). There you'll also meet with thousands and ten thousands that have gone before us to that place. None of them is hurtful, but loving and holy; everyone walking in the sight of God, and standing in his presence, accepted by him for ever. There we'll see the elders with their golden crowns (Rev. 4:4); the holy virgins with their golden harps (Rev. 14:1–5); and men whom the world cut to pieces, men who were burnt in flames, eaten by beasts, drowned in seas, for the love that they bear to the Lord of the place. And they will all be well and clothed with immortality as with a garment' (John 12:25; 2 Cor. 4:2–4).

'Just listening to this thrills my heart. But are these things actually for us? How shall we get to take part in it all?'

'The Lord, the Governor of that country, has told us in

this book. The gist of it is that if we really want to have it, he'll give it freely' (Isa. 55:1–2; John 6:37; 7:37; Rev. 21:6; 22:17).

'Well, my good friend, am I glad to hear all this! Come on, let's get a move on.'

'I can't go as fast as I'd like, because of this burden on my back.'

Now in my dream I saw that just as they had ended this conversation they approached a very miry bog that was in the middle of the plain, and since neither of them was paying attention they suddenly fell into it. The name of the bog was the Slough of Despond. They wallowed in it for a time, badly covered with the mud and because of the burden that was on his back Christian began to sink.

Then Pliable said, 'Ha! Christian, where are you now?'

'To be honest,' said Christian, 'I don't know.'

Pliable began to feel indignant. Angrily he said to his companion, 'Is this the happiness you've talked about all this time? If we have such bad luck right from the word go, what can we expect between now and the end of our journey? If I get out of this alive you can possess that brave new world all by yourself.' And with that he gave a few desperate struggles and finally got out of the bog on the side nearest to his own house. So away he went, and Christian didn't see him again.

Christian was left to stumble about in the Slough of Despond all by himself. Even so, he struggled hard to reach the side which was farthest from his house and nearest to the wicket-gate. He managed this, but couldn't get out because of the burden on his back. But in my dream I saw a man called Help come up to him and ask him what he was doing down there.

'Sir,' said Christian, 'I was told to go this way by a man called Evangelist, who also directed me to that gate over there so that I might escape the coming disaster. As I was going there, I fell in here.'

'But why didn't you look for the steps?' asked Help.

'Fear pursued me so closely that I fled the nearest way, and fell in.'

Then Help said, 'Give me your hand.'

So Christian gave him his hand, and Help lifted him out, stood him on firm ground, and sent him on his way (Ps. 40:2).

Then I stepped up to the man who had lifted Christian out, and said, 'Sir, since it is on the way from the City of Destruction to the gate over there, why is it that this bog is not filled in so that the poor travellers can get to the gate more safely?'

And he said to me, 'This miry bog is the kind of place that can't be repaired: all the scum and filth that accompany conviction for sin run endlessly down into it. So it's called the Slough of Despond. Whenever a sinner wakes up to his lost condition many fears and doubts rise up in his soul, many discouraging worries, all of which get together and settle in this place. And this is the reason for the bad state of this ground.

'It's not the king's wish that this place should remain so bad (Isa. 35:3–4). His labourers, under the direction of his majesty's surveyors, have been employed for more than these sixteen hundred years on this patch of ground to see if perhaps it might be improved. Yet, to my knowledge,' he continued, 'it has swallowed up at least twenty thousand cartloads, indeed millions, of wholesome instructions which have been brought in all seasons from all over the king's dominions to try and mend it. And those who know say they are the best possible materials for restoring the ground. But it is still the Slough of Despond. And so it will be when they have done all they can.'

'At the direction of the Lawgiver, some good strong steps have been placed through the very middle of the bog,' Help continued. 'But whenever this place spews out its filth – as it does when the weather changes – these steps can hardly be seen. Or if they are seen, in the dizziness of their heads, men step aside, and are then bogged down despite the steps. But the ground is good once they've got in at the gate' (1 Sam. 12:23).

Now in my dream I saw that by this time Pliable had reached home. So his neighbours came to visit him. Some of them called him wise for coming back; some called him a fool for risking his life in the first place; again, others mocked his cowardliness. 'Surely,' they said, 'since you began the venture . . . I wouldn't have been so base as to have given up because of a few difficulties!' So Pliable sat skulking among them. But at last he got his confidence back, and then they all changed their tune and began to deride poor Christian behind his back.

So much for Pliable.

Worldly-Wiseman

Now as Christian was walking all alone he spotted someone far off, coming over the fields towards him, and it so happened that their paths crossed. The gentleman's name was Mr Worldly-Wiseman and he lived in the town of Carnal-Policy, a very great town, not far from where Christian came from. This man had some inkling of who Christian was, for news of Christian's departure from the City of Destruction had been talked about a great deal. He had heard of Christian not only in the town where he lived, but also because he was the talk of the town in other places. So Mr Worldly-Wiseman, having guessed it was Christian from his laboured walk, and his sighs and groans, began to talk to him.

'Hello my good man! Where're you off to in such a burdened state?' asked Mr Worldly-Wiseman.

'Burdened state indeed! As great, I think, as any poor wretch has ever had to endure! And since you ask me, I'll tell you, sir. I'm going to that wicket-gate over there ahead of me. I'm told it's there that I'll be shown what to do about my heavy burden.'

'Do you have a family – a wife and children?'

'Yes, but I'm so laden down with this burden that I can't be happy with them as I used to be. I think I should live as if I had none' (1 Cor 7:29).

'Will you listen to me if I give you some advice?'

'If it's good I will because I'm in need of some good advice.'

'I would advise you, then, to get rid of your burden as quickly as you can because you'll never be settled in your mind until you do. Nor will you be able to enjoy the benefits of the blessings God has given you.'

'That's exactly what I'm trying to do — to be rid of this heavy burden. But it's impossible for me to get it off myself. Nor is there a man in our country who can take it off my shoulders. That's why I'm going this way, as I told you, to be rid of my burden.'

'Who told you to go this way to get rid of it?'

'A man who seemed to me to be a very great and honourable person. His name, as I remember, is Evangelist.'

'Curse him for his advice! There isn't a more dangerous and troublesome path in the world, as you'll find out if you do what he says. I notice you've encountered something already — I can see the filth of the Slough of Despond on you. That bog marks the beginning of the sorrows that accompany anyone who goes that way. Listen to me, I'm older than you. If you continue this way you're very likely to meet exhaustion, pain, hunger, danger, nakedness, sword, lions, dragons, darkness and, in a word, death, and who knows what else! These things are absolutely true. They've been confirmed by many witnesses. And why should a man carelessly throw himself away like that by paying attention to a stranger?'

'Why, sir, this burden on my back is far worse than all these things you've mentioned. I feel as if I don't care what I meet on the way if I can also meet with deliverance from my burden.'

'How did you come by your burden in the first place?' asked Mr Worldly-Wiseman.

'By reading this book that I'm holding.'

'I thought so! The same thing has happened to other weak men. They go berserk through meddling with things too high for them. This madness not only unmans men (as I see it has done to you), but makes them run off on desperate ventures to get they know not what.'

'I know what I want; it's relief from my heavy burden.'

'But why seek relief in this way since it brings so many dangers, and especially since, if you'd only be patient and hear me out, I could show you how to get what you want without those dangers? Yes, the remedy is at hand. And, let me add, instead of those dangers you'll find safety, friendship and happiness.'

'Sir, let me in on this secret.'

'Why, in that village over there, the one called Morality, a gentleman called Legality lives. He's a sensible type with a good reputation and has the ability to help men get rid of your kind of burden. Indeed, to my knowledge he's done a great deal of good in this way. Apart from this, he knows how to cure those people who are just about out of their mind with their burdens. As I said, you can go to him, and be quickly helped. His house isn't quite a mile from here, and if he's not at home himself, he has a good-looking son, called Civility, who can do what you want, come to that, as well as the old gentleman himself. That's where you can be eased of your burden, and if you don't feel like going back to your former way of life, as indeed I wouldn't wish you to, you can send for your wife and children, and settle in this village, where houses are standing empty right now. You could buy one at a reasonable price, and live well there, and cheaply. And to crown your happiness, you can be sure you'll live a respected and respectable life among honest neighbours, in good style, bringing credit to yourself.'

Now Christian was somewhat nonplussed by this. But soon he concluded that if what this gentleman had said was true, his wisest course of action would be to take his advice.

And with that he went on: 'Sir, please direct me to this honest man's house. Which way is it?'

'Do you see that high hill over there?' (Mount Sinai)

'Yes, very clearly,' Christian said.

'Go by that hill and the first house you come to is his.'

So Christian turned off his course to go to Mr Legality's house for help. But when he got close to the hill it seemed too high. Furthermore, the side of the hill which was next to the road hung over so much that Christian was afraid to venture near in case the hill fell on his head. So he stood still, not knowing what to do. His burden, too, seemed heavier than when he had been on his course. And flashes of fire came out of the hill, which made Christian afraid that he would be burned (Exod. 19:16–18). He began to sweat and tremble with fear (Heb. 12:21).

Then just as Christian was feeling sorry that he had taken Mr Worldly-Wiseman's advice he saw Evangelist coming to meet him. At the sight of him Christian began to blush with shame. Evangelist drew closer and closer and coming right up to Christian looked at him with a severe and dreadful expression on his face. Then he began to reason with Christian.

'What can you hear, Christian?' Evangelist asked.

Christian didn't know how to reply to this, so he stood in silence.

Then Evangelist went on, 'Aren't you the man I found crying outside the walls of the City of Destruction?'

'Yes, dear sir, I am the man,' said Christian.

'Didn't I show you the way to the little wicket-gate?'

'Yes, dear sir,' said Christian.

'How is it, then, that you've turned away so quickly? You're well off course now.'

'Soon after I had got over the Slough of Despond I met a gentleman who persuaded me that I might find a man in the village ahead who could take off my burden.'

'What was he?'

'He looked like a gentleman. He talked a great deal and

he finally got me to yield. So I came here. But when I saw this hill, and the way it hangs over the path, I stood stock-still in case it fell on my head.'

'What did that gentleman say to you?'

'He asked me where I was going, and I told him.'

'And what did he say then?'

'He asked me if I had a family, and I told him, but added that I'm so weighed down with this burden on my back that I can't be happy with them as I once was.'

'And what did he say then?'

'He urged me to get rid of my burden as quickly as possible. And I told him that was what I was seeking to do. I said, "This is why I'm going to that gate over there, to receive further instructions on how I can get to the place of deliverance." So he said he'd show me a better way. He said it was a shorter route, and one not so full of difficulties as the way you'd sent me on, sir. This way, he said, leads to the house of a gentleman who has the ability to take off these burdens. So I believed him. I turned out of that way into this in the hope that I might soon be rid of my burden. But when I came to the place, and saw things as they are, as I said, I stopped for fear of danger. And now I don't know what to do.'

Then Evangelist said, 'Wait, while I show you the words of God.' So Christian waited, trembling.

Then Evangelist said, 'Do not refuse him who warns you, for if they did not escape him who warned them on earth, how much less shall we escape if we turn away him who warns us from heaven?' (Heb. 12:25). In addition, he said, 'Now the just shall live by faith; but if he shrinks back, I will not be pleased with him' (Heb. 10:38).

Then he applied those words in this way: 'You're that man who is running into this misery. You've begun to reject the advice of the Most High and to draw back from the way of peace, almost risking your own destruction.'

Then Christian fell down at Evangelist's feet as if dead, and sobbed, 'God help me! I'm ruined!'

At this Evangelist caught him by the right hand and said, 'All the sins and blasphemies of men will be forgiven them; stop doubting and believe' (Matt. 12:31; John 20:27). Then Christian revived a little and stood up trembling, standing in front of Evangelist as before.

Evangelist went on, 'This time, pay more attention to what I tell you. I'm going to show you who it was who deluded you, and also who it was he sent you to. The man you met is someone called Worldly-Wiseman. He's rightly named, partly because he speaks only from the viewpoint of this world (1 John 4:5) — that's why he always goes to church in the town of Morality — and partly because he prefers his doctrine since it saves him from the cross (Gal. 6:12). So because he wants to create a good impression he seeks to turn people away from what I say, though it is right.

'Now there are three things about this man's advice which you must utterly hate.

'First, his turning you off the way.

'Second, his efforts to make the cross seem detestable.

'Third, his setting your feet on the road that leads to death.

'First, you must hate the way he turned you off course — yes, and the way you agreed to it. You rejected the advice of God, for the advice of a Worldly-Wiseman. The Lord says, "Make every effort to enter through the narrow door" (Luke 13:24) — the gate to which I send you; "For small is the gate that leads to life, and only a few find it" (Matt. 7:14). This wicked man turned you away from this little wicket-gate, and from the path to it, bringing you almost to destruction. So hate his turning you out of the way, and hate yourself for listening to him.

'Second, you must loathe the way he works hard to make the cross seem detestable. For you are to regard the cross as of greater value than the treasures in Egypt (Heb. 11:26). Besides, the king of glory has told you that the man who loves his life will lose it; and anyone who comes after him and does not hate his father and mother, his wife and children, his brothers and sisters – yes, even his own life – cannot be my disciple (Matt. 10:38; Mark 8:35; Luke 14.26; John 12.25). So I say, you must utterly hate any doctrine which makes an effort to persuade you that death will come through what, in fact, the truth teaches is the only way you can have eternal life.

'Third, you must hate his setting your feet on the road that leads to death.

'In addition, you must think about the man he sent you to. Think how that man was completely unable to deliver you from your burden. His name is Legality and he's the son of the slave woman who lives in slavery with her children (Gal. 4:22–7). In a mysterious way, Legality is this Mount Sinai, which you feared would fall on your head. Now if the woman and her children are in slavery, how can you expect them to set you free? This Legality is not able to set you free from your burden. To this day no one has ever rid himself of his burden through Legality nor is anyone ever likely to. By observing the law no one will be justified, because by the deeds of the law no man living can be rid of his burden. Therefore Mr Worldly-Wiseman is an alien, and Mr Legality is a cheat. As for his son Civility, in spite of his affected manner, he is merely a hypocrite, and certainly cannot help you. Believe me, all this blabber that you have heard from these stupid men is just designed to trick you out of your salvation by turning you from the way in which I set you.'

Then Evangelist called out loudly to the heavens to confirm what he'd said. Upon this, words and fire came out of the mountain under which poor Christian was standing, and made the hairs on his flesh stand on end. These were the words: 'All who rely on observing the law are under a curse, for it is written, "Cursed is everyone who does not continue to do everything written in the Book of the Law"' (Gal. 3:10).

Now Christian expected nothing but death and began to

cry out bitterly. He cursed the day he met Mr Worldly-Wiseman, calling himself a thousand fools for listening to his advice. He was also terribly ashamed to think that this man's arguments, which stemmed only from the flesh, should have prevailed upon him and caused him to give up the right way. Then he turned his attention once again to Evangelist.

'Sir, what do you think? Is there any hope? May I retrace my steps and go on up to the wicket-gate? Won't I be abandoned, and sent back from there in disgrace? I'm sorry I've listened to this man's advice, but can my sin be forgiven?'

Then Evangelist said to him, 'Your sin is very great for through it you've committed two evils. You've forsaken the way that is good, and walked along a forbidden path. Yet the man at the gate will receive you, for he has goodwill towards men. Only beware of turning away again, lest you're destroyed on the way, for his wrath can flare up in a moment' (Ps. 2:12).

Then Christian set about returning, and Evangelist, after he had kissed him, smiled at him, and sent him off with God's blessing.

The Wicket-Gate

So Christian hurried on. He neither spoke to anyone on the way, nor, if anyone spoke to him, would he trust himself to give a reply. He journeyed like someone walking on forbidden ground. He didn't feel safe until he'd once again found the path which he'd left in order to follow Mr Worldly-Wiseman's advice.

So time passed and Christian arrived at the gate. Now above the gate were the words, 'Knock, and the door will be opened' (Matt. 7:8). So he knocked. He knocked a number of times, calling:

May I now enter here? Will he within
Open to sorry me, though I have bin
An undeserving rebel? Then shall I
Not fail to sing his lasting praise on high.

At last a person of authority – called Goodwill – came to the gate. Goodwill asked, 'Who's there? Where are you from? And what do you want?'

'This is a poor burdened sinner,' said Christian. 'I come from the City of Destruction, but I'm going to Mount Zion to be delivered from the wrath to come. Sir, I've been informed that the way there is through this gate, and I want to know if you're willing to let me in.'

'I am willing, with all my heart,' replied Goodwill, opening the gate.

As Christian was stepping in, Goodwill pulled him over the threshold. 'Why did you do that?' asked Christian.

Goodwill told him, 'A little way from this gate a strong castle has been built and Beelzebub is its captain. From there he and the others with him shoot arrows at those who come up here, hoping to kill them before they can get in.'

Then Christian said, 'I'm full of joy – and fear too.'

When Christian was safely in, the man at the gate asked who had directed him there.

'Evangelist told me to come here and knock as I did,' explained Christian. 'He also said that you, sir, would tell me what I must do.'

'An open door is before you which no one can shut,' said Goodwill.

So Christian said, 'Now I'm beginning to reap the benefits of the risks I've taken.'

'How is it that you came alone?' asked Goodwill.

'None of my neighbours saw their danger as I saw mine.'

'Did any of them know you were coming?'

'Yes, my wife and children saw me set off, and called after me to turn back. Also some of my neighbours stood crying, and calling to me to return. But I put my fingers in my ears, and hurried on.'

'But didn't anyone follow you to persuade you to go back?'

'Yes, two: Obstinate and Pliable. When they saw they couldn't succeed, Obstinate returned, ranting and railing, but Pliable came on with me a little way.'

'And why didn't he continue?'

'He did. Indeed both of us came on together until we reached the Slough of Despond, which we suddenly fell into. Then my neighbour Pliable felt discouraged, and wouldn't venture further. So he climbed out again on to the side nearer to his own house, and told me I could possess the brave new country alone. He went his way, and I came mine; he followed Obstinate and I came to this gate.'

Then Goodwill said, 'Poor fellow, does heavenly splendour mean so little to him that he thinks it's not worth risking a few difficulties to obtain it?'

Christian said, 'I've told the truth about Pliable, but if I should also tell all the truth about myself it would seem as though I'm no better than he. True, Pliable went back to his own house, but I also turned aside to tread the way of death, after being persuaded by the worldly arguments of a man called Mr Worldly-Wiseman.'

'Oh! Did he come across you? Did he want you to seek relief at the hands of Mr Legality? They're both of them downright cheats. And did you take his advice?'

'Yes, as far as I dared. I went to find Mr Legality until I thought the mountain by his house would fall on my head. Then I was forced to stop.'

'That mountain has been the death of many, and will be the death of many more. It's a good thing you escaped being dashed to pieces by it.'

'Honestly, I've no idea what would have become of me there if Evangelist had not met me again. He found me when I was down in the dumps and wondering what to do. It was by God's mercy that he came to me, otherwise I'd never have come here. But now here I am, such as I am, more fit for death by that mountain, than to stand like this talking with you, my lord. What a kindness this is! Despite everything I'm still admitted here!'

Goodwill said, 'We raise no objections against anyone. It doesn't matter what they've done before coming here, they'll never be driven away (John 6:37). So, my dear Christian, come a little way with me, and I'll teach you about the way you must travel. Look ahead. Do you see this narrow path? That's the way you must go. It was marked out by the patriarchs and prophets, by Christ and his apostles, and it is as straight as a rule can make it. This is the way you must walk.'

'But,' Christian said, 'are there no turnings or bends which could make a stranger lose his way?'

'Yes, many paths lead off into another road lower than this, but they're crooked and wide. You can distinguish the right way from the wrong, because only the right way is straight and narrow' (Matt. 7:14).

Then in my dream I saw that Christian asked Goodwill if he could help him take off the burden that was on his back, because he'd still not got rid of it, nor could he without help.

Goodwill said to Christian, 'Be content to bear your burden until you come to the place of deliverance. There it will fall from your back by itself.'

Christian then began to get ready for his journey and Goodwill told him that when he had gone some distance from the gate, he would come to the house of the Interpreter. He said that Christian should knock at his door and the Interpreter would show him some excellent things. Then Christian took leave of his friend, who again bid him God-speed.

The Interpreter's House

Christian went on until he came to the Interpreter's house.

He knocked over and over again until at last someone came to the door and asked who was there.

Christian said, 'Sir, I'm a traveller, and I've been told by an acquaintance of the owner of this house that it would be good for me to call here. I'd therefore like to speak with the master of the house.'

So the servant called for the master of the house who, after a little while, came to Christian and asked him what he wanted.

'Sir,' said Christian, 'I've come from the City of Destruction and am travelling to Mount Zion. I was told by the man who stands at the gate at the top of this road that if I called here you would show me some excellent things, things that would help me on my journey.'

Then the Interpreter said, 'Come in. What I'll show you will do you good.'

He commanded his servant to light a candle and told Christian to follow him. First he took Christian into a private room and told his servant to open a door. When he had done this Christian saw a picture of a person of very great importance hanging against the wall. This was what it looked like: the man's eyes were lifted up to heaven; he held the best of books in his hands; the law of truth was written on his lips; and the world was behind his back. He stood as if he pleaded with men, and a crown of gold hung over his head.

Then Christian said, 'What does it mean?'

The Interpreter explained: 'The man whose picture this is, is one in a million. He can become a father (1 Cor. 4:15), endure the pains of childbirth (Gal. 4:19) and be like a mother caring for her little children when they are born (1 Thess. 2:7). His eyes are lifted up to heaven, the best of books is in his hands, and the law of truth is written on his lips, to show you that his work is to know and unfold dark things to sinners. He is standing as if he pleaded with men, with the world cast behind him, and a crown over his head, to show that he slights and despises the things of the present for the love he has for his master's service, and therefore he is sure to possess glory as his reward in the world to come.'

'Now,' said the Interpreter, 'I've shown you this picture first because this is a picture of the man, the only man, whom the lord of the place you travel to has authorised to be your guide in whatever difficulties you encounter on the way. So make careful note of what I have shown you, and keep it firmly in mind, lest in your travels you meet with some who pretend to lead you aright, but whose way goes down to death.'

Then the Interpreter took Christian by the hand, and led him into a very large parlour. It was full of dust, because it was never swept. After he had looked at it a little while, the Interpreter called for a man to sweep it. When he began to sweep, thick dust flew up so that Christian was almost choked. Then the Interpreter called a maid standing by. 'Bring some water and sprinkle the room,' he said. When she had done this, it was swept and cleaned with no trouble.

Christian asked, 'What does this mean?'

The Interpreter answered, 'This parlour is the heart of a man who has never been sanctified by the sweet grace of the gospel. The dust is his original sin and inward corruption which have defiled his whole personality. The one who began to sweep at first is the law; but the one who brought water, and sprinkled it, is the gospel. You saw how, as soon as the first man began to sweep, the dust flew about so much that it was impossible to clean the room. You were almost choked instead. This is to show you that the law, instead of cleansing the heart from sin, makes sin spring into life. The law gives strength to sin, and then goes on to increase sin's strength within the soul, even as it reveals and forbids it, because it doesn't have the power to subdue it (Rom. 5:20; 7:9; 1 Cor. 15:56).

'Again, you saw the maid lay the dust by sprinkling the floor, and then contentedly clean the room, to show you that when the gospel comes into the heart with its sweet and precious power then sin is vanquished and subdued. The soul is made clean through its faith and fit for the king of glory to inhabit' (John 15:3; Acts 15:9; Rom. 16:25–6; Eph. 5:26).

Then in my dream I saw that the Interpreter took Christian by the hand and led him to a little room where two small children each sat in his own chair. The name of the elder was Passion, and the younger, Patience. Passion seemed to be very discontented, but Patience was quiet.

Then Christian asked, 'Why is Passion so cross?'

The Interpreter answered, 'Their master wants Passion to wait for the best things until the beginning of next year, but he wants it all now. Patience is willing to wait.'

Then I saw someone come to Passion with a bag of treasure and pour it at his feet. Passion eagerly picked it all up and laughed Patience to scorn. But I saw that very soon Passion had squandered the lot and had nothing left but his rags.

Then Christian said to the Interpreter, 'Explain this more fully to me.'

So the Interpreter said, 'These two lads are types. Passion stands for the people of this world, and Patience for the people of the world to come. As you can see, Passion wants to have everything now, this year, that is to say, in this world. The people of this world are like that. They must have all their good things now, they can't wait till next year, that is, until the next world, for their share. That proverb, "A bird in the hand is worth two in the bush", carries more weight with them than all the divine promises of good in the world to come. But as you saw, Passion quickly squandered everything, and was soon left with nothing but rags. That's how it will be with all such people at the end of this world.'

Then Christian said, 'Now I see that Patience is wiser, and for a number of reasons. First, because he waits for the best things and second because he will still possess his glory when the other has nothing but rags.'

'And you may add another,' said the Interpreter. 'The glory of the next world will never wear out, whereas these things are suddenly gone. So Passion doesn't have much reason to laugh at Patience because he had his good things first. Patience will have more reason to laugh at Passion, because he had his best things last. For *first* must give place to *last*; *last* still has his time to come and gives place to nothing, for there is no one else to succeed. He, then, who has his share *first* must spend it over the course of time; but he that has his share *last* will have it for all time. So it's said of Dives, "In your lifetime you received your good things, while Lazarus received bad things, but now he is comforted here"' (Luke 16:25).

'I can see it's not best to covet things that belong to now, but to wait for the things to come,' said Christian.

'What you say is the truth: "For what is seen is temporary, but what is unseen is eternal" (2 Cor. 4:18). But, though this is true, yet, because things in the present and our bodily appetites are so closely related one to another, and because things to come and our worldly feelings are such strangers to one another, the first of these pairs suddenly fall into friendship, and the second are far apart.'

Then in my dream I saw the Interpreter take Christian by the hand and lead him into a place where there was a fire burning against a wall, and someone standing by, throwing a great deal of water on it to put it out. But the fire kept burning higher and hotter.

Then Christian said, 'What's the meaning of this?'

The Interpreter answered, 'This fire is the work of grace in the heart. The one who throws water on it to extinguish it is the devil. But, as you can see, in spite of that the fire burns higher and hotter. I'll show you the reason for that.'

He took him behind the wall where he saw a man holding a container of oil, out of which he continually and secretly threw oil into the fire.

Then Christian said, 'What does this mean?'

The Interpreter answered, 'This is Christ. With the oil of his grace he continually maintains the work already begun in the heart. In this way, no matter what the devil can do, the souls of Christ's people remain full of grace (2 Cor. 12:9). And you saw the man standing behind the wall to keep the fire going to teach you that it's hard for people being tempted to see how this work of grace is maintained in the soul.'

Once again the Interpreter took Christian by the hand. He led him into a pleasant place where a magnificent palace, beautiful to look at, had been built and Christian was delighted with the sight. On the top of it he saw people walking who were clothed all in gold.

Then Christian asked, 'May we go there?'

The Interpreter took him and led him up towards the door of the palace. And what a sight! At the door a huge gathering of people waited to go in, longing, but not daring to enter. A little away from the door a man sat at a table with a book and inkhorn in front of him. He was taking the names of the people who could enter the palace. Christian saw that many men in armour were standing on guard outside the doorway, resolved to do what damage and harm they could to whoever wanted to enter. This quite amazed Christian. Everyone began to move back for fear of the armed men, but at last Christian saw a man with a very determined expression on his face come up to the man who sat there writing.

'Set down my name, sir,' he said. This accomplished, the man drew his sword and put on his helmet. He then rushed at the door and the armed men, who retaliated with deadly force. But the man, not at all discouraged, fell to cutting and hacking most fiercely. After receiving and inflicting many wounds he cut his way through all his opponents, and pressed forward to the palace (Acts 14:22). At this a pleasant voice could be heard by those who were inside, and even by those who walked on the top of the palace. It said,

Come in, come in;
Eternal glory thou shalt win.

So the strong man went in, and was given clothes to wear like those within the palace. Then Christian smiled. 'I really think I know the meaning of this,' he said.

'Now,' said Christian, 'let me go there.'

'No,' said the Interpreter, 'wait till I have shown you a little more, and after that you can go on your way.'

So he took him by the hand again, and led him into a very dark room, where a man sat in an iron cage.

Now the man seemed very sad: he sat looking down to the ground, his hands clasped together, and he sighed as if his heart would break.

'What does this mean?' asked Christian.

The Interpreter told him to talk with the man.

So Christian said, 'Who are you?'

The man answered, 'I am who I was not once.'

'Who were you once?' asked Christian.

'I was once a good believer. Both in my own eyes and in the eyes of others I was growing in the faith. Once I thought I was set for the Celestial City, and had a quiet confidence and joy that I'd get there' (Luke 8:13).

'Well, who are you now?'

'Now I'm a man of despair, shut up in despair, as I'm shut up in this iron cage. I can't get out; oh, *now* I can't.'

'But how did you come to be in this condition?'

'I left off being alert and self-controlled. I dropped the reins on the neck of my lusts. I sinned against the light of the word, and the goodness of God. I've grieved the Spirit, and he's gone. I tempted the devil, and he's come to me; I've provoked God to anger, and he's left me. I've hardened my heart till I *cannot* repent.'

Then Christian said to the Interpreter, 'But is there no hope for such a man as this?'

'Ask him,' said the Interpreter.

So Christian asked, 'Is there no hope? Must you be kept

in this iron cage of despair?'

'No, none at all,' said the man.

'Why? The Son of the Blessed is full of pity.'

'I've crucified the Son of God all over again (Heb. 6:6). I've despised his person (Luke 19:14). I've despised his righteousness. I've treated his blood as an unholy thing. I've insulted the Spirit of grace (Heb. 10:26–9). So I have shut myself out of all the promises, and now there remains nothing but threatenings, dreadful threatenings, fearful threatenings of certain judgment and fiery fury, which shall devour me like an enemy.'

'Why did you bring yourself into this condition?' Christian asked.

'For the passions, pleasures, and advantages of this world. In these enjoyments I promised myself considerable delight. But now every one of those things bites me and gnaws at me like a burning worm.'

'But can't you repent and turn?'

'God has denied me repentance. His word gives me no encouragement to believe. Indeed, he himself has shut me up in this iron cage and all the men in the world cannot let me out. Oh eternity! Eternity! How shall I grapple with the misery that I must meet in eternity!'

Then the Interpreter said to Christian, 'Remember this man's misery. Let it be an everlasting warning to you.'

'Well,' said Christian, 'this is fearful! God help me to be alert and self-controlled, and to pray that I may shun the cause of this man's misery. Sir, isn't it time for me to go on my way now?'

'Wait till I've shown you one more thing, and then you can go your way.'

So the Interpreter took Christian by the hand again, and led him into a room where a man was getting out of bed. As he put on his clothes he shook and trembled.

'Why does he tremble like this?' asked Christian.

The Interpreter then asked the man to tell Christian the reason. So he began, 'Last night, as I was asleep, I dreamed. Before my eyes the heavens grew immensely black. It thundered and lightning struck in a terrifying way, which sent me into an agony. As I looked up in my dream I saw the clouds race by at an unusual pace. And then I heard a great trumpet call, and saw a man sitting on a cloud, attended by thousands of the heavenly host. They were all in flaming fire and the heavens themselves were a burning flame.

'Then I heard a voice, saying, "Arise, you dead, and come to judgment"; and with that the rocks split, the graves opened, and the dead came out (1 Cor. 15; 1 Thess. 4; Jude v.15; 2 Thess. 1:7; Rev. 20:11–14). Some of them were extremely glad and looked upwards; some sought to hide themselves under the mountains. Then I saw the man who sat upon the cloud open the book and bid the world draw near (Ps. 1:1–3; Isa. 26:21; Mic. 7:16–17). Yet, because of a fierce flame that sprang up in front of him, a suitable distance lay between the judge and the prisoners at the bar (Dan. 7:9–10; Mal.3:2–3).

'And I also heard it proclaimed to those who attended the man seated on the cloud, "Gather together the weeds, chaff, and stubble, and cast them into the burning lake" (Matt. 3:12; 13:30; Mal. 4:1). And with that the bottomless pit opened just where I was standing. Out of its mouth billowed smoke, and coals of fire, with hideous noises. And those same attendants were told, "Gather the wheat into the barn" (Luke 3:17). After that I saw many people caught up together and carried away into the clouds (1 Thess. 4:16–17); but I was left behind. I too sought to hide, but I could not, for the man who sat upon the cloud still kept his eye upon me. My sins came to mind, and my conscience accused me on every side (Rom. 2:14–15). And then I woke up from my sleep.'

'But what was it that made you so afraid of this sight?' asked Christian.

'Why, I thought that the day of judgment had come, and that I wasn't ready for it. But what frightened me most was that the angels gathered up some people, and left me behind. Also the pit of hell opened her mouth just where I was standing. My conscience, too, accused me and it seemed that the judge didn't take his eyes off me, and his face was full of wrath.'

Then the Interpreter asked Christian, 'Have you considered all these things?'

'Yes,' said Christian, 'and they fill me with hope and fear.'

'Well, keep all these things in your mind so that they may be a spur in your side to urge you forward in the way you must go.' So Christian began to get ready for his journey.

Then the Interpreter said, 'May the Comforter always be with you, dear Christian, to guide you in the way that leads to the city.'

So Christian went on his way, saying,

Here I have seen things rare and profitable;
Things pleasant, dreadful, things to make me stable
In what I have begun to take in hand:
Then let me think on them, and understand
Wherefore they shew'd me were; and let me be
Thankful, O good Interpreter, to thee.

The Cross and the Contrast

Now in my dream I saw that the highway along which Christian was to travel was closed in on either side by a wall, and that wall was called Salvation (Isa. 26:1). So up this way burdened Christian ran, but not without great difficulty because of the load on his back.

He ran till he came to a slight upward slope, on the top of which stood a cross. A little below it, at the bottom, was a tomb. I saw in my dream that just as Christian came up to the cross his burden came loose from his shoulders, and fell off his back. It began to tumble downhill, and continued rolling till it came to the mouth of the tomb, where it fell in, and I saw it no more.

How glad and light-hearted Christian was! With a happy heart he said, 'He has given me rest by his sorrow, and life by his death.' Then he stood still for a while to look and wonder. He found it very surprising that the sight of the cross should ease him of his burden like this. He gazed and gazed till the springs in his head sent tears down his cheeks (Zech. 12:10).

Now as he stood looking and weeping three Shining Ones approached him. They greeted him with the words, 'Peace be to you'. The first said to him, 'Your sins are forgiven' (Mark 2:5); the second stripped him of his rags, and dressed him in a fresh set of clothes. The third set a mark on his forehead, and gave him a scroll with a seal on it (Zech. 3:4; Eph. 1:13). He told him to look at this as he ran, and to hand it in at the Celestial Gate. Then they went on their way. Christian gave three leaps for joy, and went off singing:

> Thus far did I come laden with my sin,
> Nor could ought ease the grief that I was in,
> Till I came hither; what a place is this!
> Must here be the beginning of my bliss?
> Must here the burden fall from off my back?
> Must here the strings that bound it to me crack?
> Blest cross! Blest sepulchre! Blest rather be
> The Man that there was put to shame for me!

I saw Christian continue until he came to the bottom of the slope, where, a little way from the path, he saw three men with fetters on their heels lying fast asleep. One was called Simple, another Sloth and the third Presumption.

Christian, seeing them asleep like that, went up to them, hoping he might wake them. He cried, 'You are like someone sleeping on the high seas, lying on top of the rigging' (Prov. 23:34). 'Wake up, and come away; if you want I'll help you get your fetters off.' He continued, 'If he that prowls around like a roaring lion is looking for someone to devour, you will certainly become a prey to his teeth' (1 Pet. 5:8).

At that they looked up at him, and began to reply like this:

Simple said, 'I can't see any danger.'

Sloth said, 'Oh, just a little more sleep.'

And Presumption said, 'Every barrel must stand on its own bottom.'

So they lay down and went to sleep again, and Christian went on his way. But it upset him to think that men in such danger should think so little of his kindness in freely offering to help them by waking them, advising them, and helping to take off their irons. And as he was troubled by this, he caught sight of two men who came tumbling over the wall on the left-hand side of the narrow way, and he hurried to catch them up. One was named Formalist, and the other Hypocrisy. As he drew near, Christian entered into conversation with them.

'Gentlemen,' Christian said, 'where've you come from and where are you off to?'

'We were born in the land of Vain-glory, and are going for praise to Mount Zion,' they replied.

'Why didn't you come in at the gate which stands at the beginning of the path?' asked Christian. 'Don't you know that it's written, "The man who does not enter the sheep pen by the gate, but climbs in by some other way, is a thief and a robber"?' (John 10:1)

They replied that all their countrymen considered it much too far to go all the way to the gate to enter, and their usual way was to take a short cut. So everyone climbed over the wall, as they had just done.

'But won't it be regarded as an offence against the Lord of the city to which we are bound, to violate his clear rules in this way?' asked Christian.

Formalist and Hypocrisy replied that Christian need not trouble his head about those things because it was traditional to do this. They said that if need be they could produce testimony bearing witness to it, which went back over a thousand years.

'But,' Christian said, 'will your practice stand a trial at law?'

They told him that without any doubt tradition that had lasted more than a thousand years would now be admitted as legal practice by any impartial judge. And besides, they said, as long as they got on to the path what did it matter which way they got in?

'If we're in, we're in,' they said. 'You're on the path, as we can see, by entering in at the gate. We're also on the path by clambering over the wall. How, then, are you better off than we?'

Christian replied, 'I'm walking by the rule of my master; you're following the ignorant devices of your own whims. You're regarded as thieves already by the Lord of the way. So I doubt that the end of the way will find you true. You came in by yourselves without his direction, and shall go out by yourselves without his mercy.'

To this they gave little response, except to tell him to look out for himself. Then I saw that they all went on, every man in his way, without much exchange between them, apart from when the two men told Christian that as far as laws and ordinances were concerned, they had no doubt that they would be as conscientious as he.

'So,' they said, 'we see no difference between us, except the coat you're wearing which was, we suspect, given you by some of your neighbours to hide the shame of your nakedness.'

Christian replied, 'You didn't come in by the door, but a man is not justified by observing the law (Gal. 2:16). And as for this coat, it was given me by the Lord of the place I'm going to, in order, as you say, to cover my nakedness. I take it as a token of his kindness to me, for I had nothing but rags before. Besides, it's what comforts me on my journey. Surely, I think, when I come to the gate of the city its Lord will think well of me, since I have his coat on my back. He freely gave me this coat on the day he stripped me of my rags. Moreover, I've a mark on my forehead which you've perhaps not noticed. One of my Lord's closest friends fixed it there the day my burden fell off my shoulders. What's more, a sealed scroll was given me to comfort me on the way. I was also told to give it in at the Celestial Gate, as a token of my certain entry. I doubt you have any of these things – you missed them because you didn't enter in at the gate.'

They said nothing to all this, but only looked at each other and laughed. Then I saw them all continue their journey, only Christian kept ahead and had no more to say to anyone but himself. That he sometimes did sorrowfully and sometimes cheerfully. He also often read from the roll that one of the Shining Ones had given him, and this refreshed him.

The Hill Difficulty

I saw then that they arrived at the foot of the Hill Difficulty where there was a spring. Two other paths led off from this spring, as well as the one which came straight from the gate; one of these paths turned to the left, and the other to the right, round the bottom of the hill. But the narrow way lay right up the hillside. Because of the climb up the side of the hill it is called Difficulty. Christian went to the spring and drank to refresh himself (Isa. 49:10). He then began to climb up the hill, saying to himself:

This hill, though high, I covet to ascend;
The difficulty will not me offend,
For I perceive the way to life lies here.
Come, pluck up, heart, let's neither faint nor fear:
Better, though difficult, the right way to go,
Than wrong, though easy, where the end is woe.

The other two men also came to the foot of the hill, but when they saw how steep and high the hill was, and that there were two other paths, they supposed that these two ways would meet up again with Christian's path on the other side of the hill and resolved to travel along those paths. (Now the name of one was Danger, and the other Destruction.) So one took Danger Road, which led him into a great wood. The other went directly up the path to Destruction, which led him into a wide field from which rose dark mountains. There he stumbled and fell, and didn't rise again.

I looked for Christian and saw him going up the hill, where he slowed from running to walking, and from walking to clambering on his hands and knees because the slope was so steep. Now about half-way up there was a pleasant arbour, made by the Lord of the hill, where tired travellers could refresh themselves. There Christian sat down to rest. Pulling his scroll from his breast, he read to his great comfort. He also began to examine the coat or garment that had been given him when he had been standing by the cross. And so, enjoying himself in this way, he at last fell into a deep sleep, which was to detain him in that place until it was almost night. And as he slept his scroll fell out of his hand. Then a man came to him and woke him up, saying, 'Go to the ant, you sluggard; consider its ways and be wise!' (Prov. 6:6). With that Christian suddenly sat up, and hurried on his way. He climbed quickly till he came to the top of the hill.

When he reached the top of the hill, two men came running at full speed towards him. The name of one was Timorous, and the other Mistrust. Christian said to them, 'Sirs, what's the matter? You're running the wrong way.'

Timorous answered that they had been going to the City of Zion, and had got past Christian's difficult place. 'But,' he continued, 'the farther we go, the more danger we meet with, so we've turned, and are going back again.'

'Yes,' said Mistrust, 'for on the path just ahead lie a couple of lions. We'd no idea whether they were asleep or not, all we could think was that if we came within reach, they'd pull us to pieces.'

Then Christian said, 'You're making me feel afraid. But where shall I fly to be safe? I can't go back to my own country, it's ripe for fire and sulphur and I shall certainly die there. But if I can get to the Celestial City, I'm sure to be safe. I must venture on. To go back is nothing but sure death; to go forward brings the fear of death, and life everlasting beyond it. I'll still go forward.'

So Mistrust and Timorous ran down the hill and Christian went on his way. But thinking again of what he had heard from the men, he felt against his breast for his scroll, so that he might read it and be encouraged. But it wasn't there. Christian was in great distress. He didn't know what to do. He wanted what used to bring relief to him, and should have been his pass into the Celestial City. He was very puzzled and didn't know what to do. At last he remembered that he had slept in the arbour on the side of the hill and falling down on his knees he asked God's forgiveness for that foolish act. Then he went back. Who can adequately describe the sorrow in Christian's heart? Sometimes he sighed, sometimes he wept. Often he was angry with himself for being foolish enough to fall asleep in a place which had been built only to provide a little refreshment for weary travellers. In this state he returned, carefully looking to one side and then the other as he went in the hope that he might find this scroll which had been his comfort so many times on his journey.

He continued on like this till he came again within sight of the arbour where he had sat and slept. But the sight of it brought a fresh surge of sorrow as he remembered all over again the evil of his sleeping.

So he kept bewailing his sinful sleep, saying, 'Oh, wretched man that I am! How could I sleep in the daytime! How could I sleep in the midst of difficulty! (1 Thess. 5:7–8; Rev. 2:4–5) How could I indulge the flesh by using that arbour to satisfy my physical needs when the Lord of the hill had erected it only for the relief of the spirits of pilgrims! How many steps have I taken in vain! This is what happened to Israel; for their sin they were sent back again by the way of the Red Sea. I am forced to tread with sorrow, when I might have walked with delight if only it had not been for this sinful sleep. How far I might have travelled on my way by this time! Now I have to tread this path three times when I need only have walked it once. Yes, and now I'm likely to be caught by the night since the day is almost over. Oh, how I wish I'd not slept!'

Now by this time Christian had come to the arbour again. There, for a while, he sat down and wept. But at last (as Christian would have it) looking sorrowfully down under the bench, there he spotted his scroll! Trembling all over he hastily picked it up and put it against his breast. Who can describe how joyful this man was when he had retrieved his roll which assured him of his life and guaranteed acceptance at the desired heaven! So he placed it against his breast, gave thanks to God for directing his eye to the spot where it lay, and with joy and tears set off again on his journey. How nimbly he ran up the rest of the hill!

Vanity Fair

As Christian went on he came to a small rise in the ground that had been made on purpose so that pilgrims might see ahead. Christian climbed up and looking forward he saw Faithful ahead of him on his journey. Christian called aloud, 'Hey! Hey! Wait! I'll be your companion.' At that Faithful looked behind him and Christian called again, 'Wait! Wait, till I catch up with you.'

But Faithful answered, 'No! My life is at stake, and the avenger of blood is behind me.'

Christian was moved by this, and exerting all his strength he quickly caught up with Faithful, and then overtook him, so that the last was first. Then Christian gave a conceited smile, because he had got ahead of his brother. But not paying careful attention to his feet, he suddenly stumbled and fell and couldn't get up again until

Faithful came to help him.

Then I saw in my dream that they went on talking very lovingly together of all the things that had happened to them on their pilgrimage. . . .

Then in my dream I saw that they saw a town in front of them called Vanity. At this town there is a fair, called Vanity Fair, which keeps going all year long. It bears the name of Vanity Fair because the town is 'lighter than vanity', and also because all that is sold, and everything that comes there, is empty vanity, as the saying of the wise goes, 'everything is meaningless' (Eccles. 1:2, 14; 2:11, 17; 11:8; Isa. 40:17).

This fair is not newly-erected, but is a thing of ancient standing. I'll show you its origins. Almost five thousand years ago pilgrims were walking to the Celestial City, as these two honest men are. Beelzebub, Apollyon and Legion, with their companions, saw from the path that the pilgrims were following that their way to the city lay through this town of Vanity, and so they contrived to set up a fair here. It was to be a fair in which trash of all sorts would be sold, and it was to last all the year long. So at this fair many goods are on offer, such as houses, lands, jobs, places, honours, positions, titles, countries, kingdoms, evil desires, pleasures; and delights of all sorts, such as prostitutes, pimps, wives, husbands, children, masters, servants, lives, blood, bodies, souls, silver, gold, pearls, precious stones, and so on.

What's more, at all times you can see conjurers, tricksters, amusements, plays, fools, mimics, swindlers and hooligans of every kind. Here to be seen also, and that for nothing, are thefts, murders, adulteries and perjuries, blood-red in colour.

In other fairs on a lesser scale there are rows and streets, all called by their proper names, each selling different commodities, and here, in the same way, you have the proper places, the rows and streets (that is, countries and kingdoms) where the commodities of this fair can be quickly found. Here is the British row, the French row, the Italian row, the Spanish row, the German row, where different sorts of empty trivia are on sale. But, as in other fairs, one commodity in particular is given pride of place. Roman goods are promoted in this fair, and only our English nation, with a few others, have taken a dislike to this.

Now, as I said, the way to the Celestial City passes right through the town where this large fair is held. And anyone who wants to go to the city, and yet not go through this town, 'must needs go out of the world'. The Prince of princes himself, when he was here, went through this town to his own country, and that on a carnival day, too. I think it was Beelzebub, the chief lord of this fair, who invited him to buy some of his trash. Indeed he would have made him Lord of the fair, if only he had bowed down to Beelzebub as he went through the town. Because he was such a VIP Beelzebub took him from street to street, and quickly showed him all the kingdoms of the world to see if he could lure that Blessed One into cheapening himself by buying some of his trash. But he paid no attention to the merchandise and left the town without laying out so much as one penny (Matt. 4:8–9; Luke 4:5–7). So this fair is an ancient thing, of long standing, and a very great fair.

Now these pilgrims, as I said, had to go through this fair, and so they did. But as they went into the fair, there was a commotion among all the people there and the whole town was in a hubbub about them. This happened for several reasons.

First, the pilgrims were wearing clothes that were quite different to any of the clothes on sale in the fair. So the people of the fair gaped at them. Some said they were fools, some that they were madmen, and some that they were outlandish foreigners (1 Cor. 4:9–10).

Second, their speech caused exactly the same bewilderment as their clothes, for few could understand what they said. These two naturally spoke the language of Canaan, but those who ran the fair were men of this world. From one end of the fair to the other Christian and Faithful were regarded as barbarians while the two pilgrims thought the same of the people of Vanity Fair.

Third, and this caused no small amusement to the stall-holders, these pilgrims set little store by all their goods. They weren't interested even in looking at them. If the sellers called them to buy, they would put their fingers in their ears, and cry, 'Turn my eyes away from worthless things'; and they would look upwards, to show that their trade and traffic was in heaven (Ps. 119:37; Phil. 3:20–1).

One tried his luck. As he saw them pass by he called out mockingly, 'What will you buy?'

But they looked seriously at him, and said, 'We buy the truth' (Prov. 23:23).

This made everyone despise the men even more, some mocking, some taunting, some insulting and some calling on others to punch them. Finally things came to a head. There was such noise and chaos in the fair that all order was lost. Word was at once brought to the great one of the fair, who quickly came down. He deputed some of his most trusted friends to seize these men who had virtually turned the fair upside down and take them in for questioning. So the men were taken in, and their interrogators asked them where they came from, where they were going and what they were doing there in such strange garb. The men told them that they were pilgrims and strangers in the world, and that they were going to their own country, which was the heavenly Jerusalem (Heb. 11:13–16). They said they'd not given the townsmen or traders any cause to abuse them in this way, and hinder them on their journey, except for one occasion, when someone asked them what they wanted to buy, and they said they wanted to buy the truth. But their interrogators thought they were lunatics and madmen, or else troublemakers who had set out to disrupt the fair.

So they took the two pilgrims and beat them. Then they smeared them with filth, and put them in a cage as a spectacle for all the men of the fair. Christian and Faithful lay there for some time, the objects of any man's sport, or malice, or revenge, and the great one of the fair laughed at all that happened to them. But the two men were patient, 'not repaying insult with insult, but with blessing' (1 Pet. 3:9), returning good words for bad, and kindness for injuries. As a result, some men in the fair, who were more observant and less prejudiced than the rest, restrained and told off the baser sort for the abuses they continually meted out to the two men. They however angrily let fly at these others, reckoning them as bad as the men in the cage. They accused these supporters of being in league with Christian and Faithful and said they should be forced to suffer their misfortune, too. The supporters replied that as far as they could see the men were quiet and sober, and intended nobody any harm. They went on to suggest that there were many who traded in that fair who deserved the cage, and the pillory, too, far more than these men whom they'd abused.

After various words had passed on both sides (the two prisoners consistently behaving very wisely and quietly in front of them), they fell to fighting among themselves, and injuring one another. So these two poor men were brought before their examiners once again, charged with being guilty of this latest disturbance in the fair. They were beaten pitilessly, irons were fastened on to them and they were led in chains up and down the fair, as an example and warning in case anybody else should speak up for them or join them. But Christian and Faithful behaved still more wisely. They received the humiliation and shame that were thrown at them with so much meekness and patience that several of the men of the fair were won over (though they were only few in comparison with the rest). This put the other side into an even greater rage, so much so that they decided the two men had got to die. They threatened that neither cage nor irons would be enough, but that they should die for the harm they'd done, and for deluding the men of the fair.

A date was fixed for their trial and condemnation and when the time came they were brought out before their enemies and charges were laid. Their judge's name was Lord Hategood. The content of their indictment was the same in each case, but the wording varied slightly. It said that they were enemies to, and disturbers of, their trade; that they had caused disturbances and divisions in the town; and had won a party to their own very dangerous opinions in contempt of the law of their prince.

Faithful began to answer. He said that he had only set himself against what had set itself against the One who is higher than the highest. And he added, 'As far as disturbing the peace goes, I've done nothing of the kind, because I'm a man of peace. The people who came over to us were won when they saw our truth and innocence, and they've only changed from the worse to the better. And as far as the king you talk of is concerned, since he's Beelzebub, the enemy of our Lord, I defy him and all his angels.'

Then a proclamation went out. It called for anyone who had anything to say for their lord and king against the prisoner at the bar to appear and give evidence. So three witnesses came – Envy, Superstition and Flatterer. They were asked if they knew the prisoner at the bar, and what they had to say for their lord the king against him.

Then Envy held forth. 'My lord, I've known this man a long time, and will attest upon my oath before this honourable bench that he is . . .'

'Wait, administer the oath,' interrupted the Judge.

So they swore him in. Then he continued, 'My lord, this man, despite his plausible name, is one of the vilest men in our country. He respects neither prince nor people, law nor tradition, but does all that he can to spread his treacherous ideas, which he calls "principles of faith and holiness". In particular I myself once heard him affirm that Christianity and the customs of our town of Vanity are diametrically opposed, and can't be reconciled. In saying this, my lord, he at once not only condemns all our laudable activities, but us also for doing them.'

Then the Judge said, 'Have you anything more to say?'

'My lord, I could say much more, only I don't want to bore the court,' said Envy. 'Yet if need be, when the other gentlemen have given their evidence, rather than let anything be left out that could get rid of him, I'll give further evidence against him.'

So Envy was asked to stand down.

Next they called Superstition, and told him to look at the prisoner. They asked him what he could say for their lord the king against the prisoner and then swore him in.

Superstition began, 'My lord, I don't know this man very well, nor do I desire to. But I could tell from a conversation that I had with him in this town the other day that he's a thorough nuisance. I heard him say that our religion is worthless and we can't please God with it. And your lordship knows what that means. It means our worship gets us nowhere, we're still in our sins, and in the end we'll be damned. That's all I have to say.'

Then Flatterer was sworn in and invited to say what he knew on behalf of their lord the king against the prisoner at the bar.

'My lord, and all you gentlemen,' began Flatterer, 'I've known this fellow for a long time, and I've heard him say things that he ought not to have said. He's raged against our noble prince Beelzebub, and has spoken with contempt of his honourable friends, the Lord Oldman, the Lord Carnal-delight, the Lord Luxurious, the Lord Desire-of-Vain-glory, my old Lord Lechery, Sir Having Greedy, and all the rest of our nobility. What's more, he's said that if all men thought like him, possibly not one of these noble men would continue to exist in this town. Besides, he hasn't been afraid to rant and rave at you, my lord, you, who are appointed to be his judge, calling you an ungodly scoundrel, and many other scandalous things. And he's smeared the characters of most of the dignitaries of our town in just the same way.'

When Flatterer had given his account, the Judge addressed the prisoner at the bar, 'You, deserter, heretic and traitor, have you heard what these honest gentlemen have testified against you?'

'May I speak a few words in my own defence?' asked Faithful.

The Judge replied, 'You, sir, don't deserve to live, you should die on the spot. But, so that everyone can see how kind we are, let's hear what you have to say – you vile deserter, you.'

Faithful spoke, 'In reply I say to Mr Envy that I've never said anything but this: any rule, or law, or custom, or people, that goes flatly against the word of God, is diametrically opposed to Christianity. If I've said anything wrong in saying this, convince me of my error and I'm willing in front of all of you to take my words back.

'As to the second charge, namely that from Mr Superstition, I only said that in the worship of God divine faith is required, but there can be no divine faith without a divine revelation of the will of God. So whatever is thrust into the worship of God that conflicts with divine revelation must have been from a man-made faith which will be of no benefit for eternal life.

'As to what Mr Flatterer said, putting on one side the accusation that I am said to rant and rave and so on, I say that the prince of this town, with all his attendant rabble named by this gentleman, are more fit for a place in hell than in this town and country, so the Lord have mercy upon me.'

So the jury went out. Their names were Mr Blindman, Mr Nogood, Mr Malice, Mr Lovelust, Mr Liveloose, Mr Heady, Mr Highmind, Mr Enmity, Mr Liar, Mr Cruelty, Mr Hatelight and Mr Implacable. When they had talked together, each one gave in his personal verdict against the accused and then they unanimously voted to give the judge a verdict of guilty.

And so Faithful was quickly condemned. He was to be

returned to the place he'd been brought from and put to the most cruel death that could be invented.

Now I saw that behind the crowds a chariot and two horses stood waiting for Faithful. As soon as his enemies had killed him, Faithful was taken up into the chariot. Immediately he was carried through the clouds and to the sound of the trumpet was taken by the nearest way to the Celestial Gate.

Christian was sent back to prison where he remained for a while. But the One who overrules all things, and held all the power of their rage within his hands, enabled Christian to escape from them.

Christian and Hopeful

Now I saw in my dream that Christian didn't go on alone. Someone whose name was Hopeful (this is what he became after observing the words and behaviour and all the suffering of Christian and Faithful at Vanity Fair) joined him as he walked. He made a brotherly pact with Christian and told him that he would be his companion. So one died to bear testimony to the truth, and another rose out of his ashes to be a companion for Christian on his pilgrimage. Hopeful also told Christian that many more of the men in the fair would, in their own time, follow after them.

Then I saw that very soon after leaving the fair they overtook someone ahead of them whose name was By-ends. They called to him, 'What town are you from, sir? And how far are you going along this path?'

He told them that he came from the town of Fairspeech, and was going to the Celestial City, but he didn't tell them his name.

'From Fairspeech!' said Christian. 'Is any good to be found there?' (Prov. 26:25)

'Yes,' said By-ends, 'I hope so.'

'Sir, what may I call you?' asked Christian.

'I'm a stranger to you and you to me,' By-ends said. 'If

you're going this way, I'll be glad of your company, if not, I must rest content.'

'This town of Fairspeech, I've heard of it, and, as far as I remember, they say it's a wealthy place,' said Christian.

'Yes, I can assure you that it is and I've very many rich relatives there.'

'Who are your relatives, if I may be so bold?' asked Christian.

'Almost the whole town, and in particular, my Lord Turnabout, my Lord Time-server, and my Lord Fairspeech, from whose ancestors that town first took its name. Also Mr Smoothman, Mr Facing-both-ways, Mr Anything; and the parson of our parish, Mr Two-tongues, who was my mother's own brother on my father's side. Well, to tell you the truth, I'm a gentleman of quality, yet my great grandfather was merely a boatman, looking one way and rowing another, and I got most of my wealth from the same occupation.'

'Are you a married man?' asked Christian.

'Yes. My wife is a very good woman, and the daughter of a good woman. She's my Lady Feigning's daughter, so she comes from a very distinguished family. She's so extremely refined that she knows how to take her refinement to everyone, from prince to pauper. It's true we differ slightly in our Christianity from those who are more religious, but only in two small points. First, we never struggle to swim against the wind and tide. Second, we are always most zealous when religion parades in his silver slippers. We do so love to walk with religion openly in the street if the sun shines, and the people applaud him.'

Then Christian moved a little aside to his companion Hopeful, and said, 'It crosses my mind that this chap is someone called By-ends, of Fairspeech, and if it is he we're in the company of as despicable a fellow as you'll find anywhere round here.'

Then Hopeful said, 'Ask him; I don't think he should be ashamed of his name.'

So Christian came up to him again and said, 'Sir, you talk as if you know something that the rest of the world doesn't know, and, if I don't miss my mark, I think I've half guessed who you are. Isn't your name Mr By-ends, of Fairspeech?'

'Certainly not! That's just a nickname given me by people who can't stand me. And I must be willing to suffer this insult, as other good men have suffered insults before me.'

'But didn't you ever give anyone cause to call you this?' Christian asked.

'Never! The worst I ever did to deserve it was that I always had the luck to judge the times and jump with the trend whatever it was, and do well for myself that way. But if things fall out that way, I'll count it a blessing. Why should malicious people load me with insults?' said By-ends.

'I thought you were the man I'd heard of,' Christian said. 'To tell you what I really think, I'm afraid this name applies to you more than you'd like us to think.'

'Well, if you like to think that, I can't help it. You'll find me good company if you'll still allow me to associate with you,' said By-ends.

'If you go with us,' Christian said, 'you must swim against the tide, which, I see, is contrary to your views. You must also own religion in his rags as well as in his silver slippers, and you must stand by him, too, when bound in irons, as well as when he walks the streets to cheers.'

'You must not impose your views, nor lord it over my faith. Leave me my liberty, and let me go with you,' said By-ends.

'Not a step farther, unless you accept what I've just said, and do as we do,' said Christian.

Then By-ends said, 'I'll never desert my old principles, since they're harmless and profitable. If I can't go with you, I must do as I did before you overtook me, and go by myself until someone overtakes me who'll be glad of my company.'

Now I saw in my dream that Christian and Hopeful left him, and kept their distance from him. But looking back one of them saw three men following Mr By-ends. As they came up to him he bowed very low and they complimented him. The men's names were Mr Hold-the-world, Mr Money-love, and Mr Saveall, men with whom Mr By-ends had formerly been acquainted. When they were young they were at school together, and were taught by a Mr Gripeman, a schoolmaster in Lovegain, which is a market-town in the county of Coveting, in the north. This school-master taught them the art of getting, either by violence, deceit, flattery, lying, or by putting on a false religious front, and these four gentlemen had acquired so much from their master's art that they could each have run such a school themselves.

Well, as I said, when they'd greeted each other in this way, Mr Money-love said to Mr By-ends, 'Who is on the road ahead of us?' For Christian and Hopeful were still within sight.

'They're a couple of distant countrymen, who in their own way are off on a pilgrimage.'

'What a shame! Why didn't they stay? We might have had their good company. I hope we are all going on a pil-grimage,' said Money-love.

'We are indeed,' said By-ends. 'But the men in front of us are so puritanical and so fond of their own ideas, and think so little of the opinions of others, that be a man never so godly, if he doesn't go along with them in every detail, they throw him right out of their company.'

'That's bad,' said Saveall. 'But we read of people who are over-scrupulous and their rigidness makes them judge and condemn everyone but themselves. But what were the points you disagreed on?'

'Why in their headstrong way they've decided that it's their duty to rush on with their journey in all weathers, while I'm for waiting for wind and tide. They're for risking everything for God at once, in one go, and I'm for taking every opportunity to hold on to my life and possessions. They're for keeping to their ideas though all the world be against them, but I'm for religion as far as the times and my safety will bear it. They're for religion even in rags and in disgrace, but I'm for religion when he walks in his golden slippers, in the sunshine, to applause.'

Then Hold-the-world said, 'Yes, and stay as you are, good Mr By-ends. As far as I'm concerned, a man's a fool, who when he's free to keep what he has, is stupid enough to lose it. Let us be "wise as serpents"; it's best "to make hay when the sun shines"; you see how the bee lies still all winter, and stirs herself only when she can have profit accompanied by pleasure. God sometimes sends rain and sometimes sunshine. If they want to be stupid enough to go through the first, we'll be content to take fine weather along with us. For my part, I'd rather have a religion that promises us the security of God's good blessings. For what reasonable man could suppose that God, since he has bestowed on us all the good things of this life, wouldn't want us to keep them, for his sake? Abraham and Solomon grew rich in religion, and Job says that a good man "shall lay up gold as dust". He must not be like the men ahead of us, if they're as you've described them.'

'I think that we're all agreed about this, and so there's no need to waste any more words,' said Saveall.

Money-love agreed, 'No, there's certainly no need for any more words on this subject. For someone who believes neither Scripture nor reason — and you see we have both on our side — doesn't know his own freedom and doesn't seek his own safety.'

'My brothers,' said By-ends, 'as you see, we're going on a pilgrimage, and, to divert our minds from such negative things give me leave to put this question to you.

'Suppose a man, a minister or tradesman, or whoever, saw in front of him the opportunity of getting the good things of this life. But the only way he could do it was by — in appearance at least — becoming extraordinarily fervent about some aspects of religion that he'd had nothing to do with before. May he not use this means to attain his end, and still be a good honest man?'

Money-love replied, 'I see what you're getting at, and, with these gentlemen's kind permission, I'll try my best to give you an answer. First, with regard to your question concerning a *minister* himself. Suppose a minister, a worthy man, but with a very small living, has his eye on a greater one, far more fat and plump. And suppose he has the opportunity to get it, by being more studious, by preaching more frequently and fervently, and, because the nature of the congregation requires it, by altering some of his principles. For my part, I see no reason why a man may not do this, and remain an honest man, provided he has a call. Ay, and he may do a great deal more as well. And I'll tell you why:

'First, his desire for a better living is lawful – that can't be contradicted, as it's been set before him by Providence. So then he may try to get it if he can without disturbing his conscience.

'Second, his desire for that living makes him more studious, a more fervent preacher, and so on, and this makes him a better man. It makes him better and it improves his talents and this accords with the mind of God.

'Third, as for complying with the feelings of his people by denying some of his principles in order to serve them, this indicates, first that he is of a self-denying temperament, second that he has a sweet and winning way, and third that he is therefore more fit for the job of minister.

'Fourth, to conclude, a minister who changes a *small* for a *great* living should not be judged as covetous. Rather, since he has thereby become better qualified and more hard-working, he should be regarded as someone who pursues his calling and the opportunity given to him to do good.

'Which brings me to the second part of the question – concerning the *tradesman* you mentioned. Suppose such a person has only a poor business but by becoming religious can widen his market, perhaps get a rich wife, or more and superior customers for his shop. For my part, I see no reason why this may not be lawfully done. My reasons are:

'First, to become religious is a virtue, however it happens.

'Second, nor is it unlawful to marry a rich wife, or get more customers for my shop.

'Third, the man who gets these by becoming religious gets what is good, from those who are good, by becoming good himself. So then, here is a good wife, and good customers, and good profit, all by becoming religious, which is good. So, to become religious to gain all these things is a good and worthwhile policy.'

This answer by Mr Money-love to Mr By-ends' question, was much applauded by all of them, and they came to the conclusion that on the whole such a course of action was very advantageous. And because, as they thought, no one was able to contradict this argument and because Christian and Hopeful were still within calling distance, they enthusiastically agreed to attack them with this question as soon as they overtook them. They were especially keen since Christian and Hopeful had opposed Mr By-ends. So they called out to the two ahead of them who stopped and waited while they caught up. But as they approached they decided that not Mr By-ends, but old Mr Hold-the-world, should present the question. They thought an answer to him would be without any remaining heat that had been kindled between Mr By-ends and these two when they had parted earlier.

So they all met up, and after a brief greeting Mr Hold-the-world put the question to Christian and his friend, and invited them to answer it if they could.

So Christian replied, 'Even a babe in religion could answer thousands of such questions. For if it's not right to follow Christ for loaves of bread – as it's not (John 6:26) – how much more horrible is it to use him and religion as a cover to seize and enjoy the world? We find that only heathens, hypocrites, devils and witches, hold your opinion.

'First, heathens. For when Hamor and Shechem wanted Jacob's daughter and cattle, and saw that the only way to get them was by being circumcised, they said to their companions, "If every male of us be circumcised, shall not their cattle, and their substance, and every beast of theirs be ours?" Their daughters and their cattle were what they were seeking, and their religion was the cover they made use of to achieve their ends. Read the whole story in Genesis 34:20–4.

'Second, the hypocritical Pharisees were also of this persuasion; they pretended to make long prayers, and intended to get widows' houses. Their judgment was greater damnation from God (Luke 20:46–7).

'Third, Judas the devil was the same. He was religious for the money bag (John 12:6), to get the contents for himself. As a result he was lost, cast away, and doomed to destruction (John 17:12).

'Fourth, Simon the magician held to this religion, too. He wanted to have the Holy Spirit to make money out of him, hence his sentence from Peter (Acts 8:18–23).

'Fifth, I can't help thinking that the man who takes up religion for the world, will throw away religion for the world. For just as surely as Judas became religious because he had designs on the world, so he also sold religion, and his Master, for the same reason.

'Therefore, to answer the question in the affirmative, as I see you've done, and to accept that as the true answer, is both un-Christian, hypocritical and devilish. And you'll get the reward your works deserve.'

Then they stood staring at one another, but weren't able to answer Christian. Hopeful also approved of the soundness of Christian's answer. So there was a great silence among them.

Mr By-ends and his company faltered and lagged behind, so that Christian and Hopeful might go ahead of them. Then Christian said to his companion, 'If these men can't stand before the sentence of men, what will they do with the sentence of God? And if they're dumb when dealt with by vessels of clay, what will they do when rebuked by the flames of a consuming fire?' (Exod. 24:17)

Then Christian and Hopeful went ahead of them again, and continued till they came to a pleasant plain called Ease, where they walked with great pleasure. But that plain was only narrow, so they were quickly over it. Now at the farther side was a small hill called Lucre, and in that hill there was a silver mine. Because of its rarity some of those who had previously passed that way had turned aside to see it. But they went too near the brink of the pit, where the ground was treacherous. It broke under their feet, and they were killed. Some had also been crippled there, and to their dying day couldn't be their own men again.

Then I saw in my dream that a little way off the road, close by the silver mine, Demas stood, looking like a very fine gentleman, and calling to passers-by to come and see. He said to Christian and his companion, 'Hi there! Come here, and I'll show you a thing or two.'

'What's so important that we've got to turn out of our way to see it?' asked Christian.

'It's a silver mine, with people digging in it for treasure. If you'll come you'll find that for only a little trouble you can set yourself up for life,' Demas said.

'Let's go and see,' said Hopeful.

'Not I,' said Christian. 'I've heard of this place, and of all the people that have been killed there. And, besides that, treasure always traps those who hunt for it. It stops them in their pilgrimage.'

Then Christian called to Demas, 'Isn't the place dangerous? Hasn't it hindered many in their pilgrimage?'

'Not very dangerous, unless you're careless.' But Demas blushed as he said this.

Then Christian said to Hopeful, 'Let's not stir a step out of our way, but keep going.'

Hopeful added, 'I bet you that if By-ends receives the same invitation when he comes up, he'll turn aside to see.'

'No doubt of it – that's what his principles tell him to do – and a hundred to one he dies there.'

Then Demas called again, 'Won't you come over and see?'

But Christian answered roundly, 'Demas, you're an enemy to the Lord of this path, and to his ways. You've already been condemned by one of his Majesty's judges for turning aside yourself. Why are you trying to get us all condemned? (2 Tim. 4:10). Besides, if we turn aside, our Lord the King will certainly hear of it and instead of facing him boldly, we'll be in disgrace when we come before him.'

Demas protested that he was one of their fellowship too; and if they'd wait just a little he'd walk with them himself.

Then Christian said, 'What's your name? Isn't it what I've called you?'

'Yes, my name is Demas; I'm the son of Abraham.'

'I know you,' Christian said. 'Gehazi was your great-grandfather, and Judas your father, and you've followed their steps. It's nothing more nor less than a trick of the devil that you're using. Your father was hanged for a traitor, and you deserve no better (2 Kings 5:20–7; Matt. 26:14–15; 27:3–5). Rest assured that when we see the King we'll tell him of your conduct.' And so they went on their way.

By this time By-ends and his companions had again come within sight, and at his first signal they went over to Demas. Now, whether they fell into the pit as they looked over the brink, or whether they went down to dig, or whether they were smothered at the bottom by the damp fumes that frequently rise up, I'm not certain, but I did observe that they were never seen again on the way.

Then Christian sang:

By-ends and silver Demas both agree;
One calls, the other runs, that he may be

A sharer in his lucre; so these two
Take up in this world, and no further go.

Now just on the other side of this plain I saw the pilgrims came to a place where an old monument was standing close by the roadside. They stopped, worried by the
strangeness of its shape, for it looked as if it had been a
woman transformed into a pillar. They stood staring and
staring at it, but for some time couldn't think what to make
of it. At last Hopeful spotted something written on the top.
It was in an unusual script and, being no scholar, he called
to Christian, who was an educated man, to see if he could
pick out the meaning. So Christian came and, after spending a little while working out the letters, he found that it
read: 'Remember Lot's wife'. He read it to his companion
and they both decided that that was the pillar of salt into
which Lot's wife was turned for looking back greedily
when she was escaping from Sodom (Gen. 19:26). This
sudden and amazing sight led to the following conversation.

'Well, brother!' Christian said. 'This comes as a timely
warning after Demas's invitation to come over and look at
Lucre Hill. Had we done as he wanted – and as you were
inclined to do – for all I know we ourselves might have
been turned into a spectacle, like this woman, for everyone
who comes after to stare at.'

'I'm sorry I was so foolish,' Hopeful said. 'It's a wonder
the same thing didn't happen to me. What's the difference
between her sin and mine? She only looked back, and I
wanted to go and see. Praise God for his grace to me! I'm
ashamed of what was in my heart.'

'Let's take careful note of what we see here so that it will
help us in the future,' Christian said. 'This woman escaped
one judgment – she didn't fall when Sodom was destroyed.
Yet she was destroyed by a second judgment. So here she
is, turned into a pillar of salt.'

'True,' added Hopeful, 'she can be both a warning and

an example to us. A warning to us to steer clear of her sin, and an example of the judgment that'll overtake any who aren't put off by this warning. So Korah, Dathan, and Abiram, with the 250 men who perished in their sin, were a lesson and an example to others (Num. 26:9–10). I wonder how Demas and his companions can stand so confidently over there looking for that treasure when this woman was turned into a pillar of salt, just for looking behind her – for we don't read that she put as much as a foot out of the way – especially as the pillar is within sight of where they are. They're bound to see her, if they'd only lift up their eyes.'

'It does make you wonder,' Christian agreed. 'And it shows how desperate they are. They're like nothing so much as thieves who pick pockets in the presence of the judge, or steal purses under the gallows. It's said of the men of Sodom that they were wicked because they were sinning greatly against the Lord (Gen. 13:13), that is, in his presence, and in spite of the kindness that he'd showed them, for the land of Sodom was like the Garden of Eden in earlier times (Gen. 13:10). This made him more angry and made their plague as hot as the Lord's fire out of heaven could make it. It follows that others like them – including these men there – who sin in his sight, right in the face of examples warning them to the contrary, must experience the severest of judgments.'

'I'm sure that's true,' said Hopeful, 'but what a mercy it is that neither you nor I, especially I, have let ourselves become such an example! This gives us cause to thank God, to fear him, and always to remember Lot's wife.'

Doubting Castle and Giant Despair

I saw then that they went on their way to a pleasant river, which David the king called 'the river of God', but John, 'the river of the water of life' (Ps. 46:4; 65:9; Ezek. 47:1–9; Rev. 22:1). Now their way lay along the bank of the river, and here Christian and his companion walked with great delight. They also drank the water from the river, which was pleasant and refreshed their weary spirits. On each side of the river banks there were green trees bearing many kinds of fruit, the leaves of which were good for medicine. They were delighted with the fruit and they ate the leaves to cure over-eating and other illnesses which come to people who get overheated through travelling. On either side of the river there was a meadow, where beautiful and rare lilies grew, and it was green all the year long. In this meadow they lay down and slept, for here they were quite safe (Ps. 23:2; Isa. 14:30). When they woke they again picked fruit from the trees, and drank the water and then lay down to sleep. In this way several days and nights went by. Then they sang:

> Behold ye how these crystal streams do glide,
> To comfort pilgrims by the highway-side.
> The meadows green, besides their fragrant smell,
> Yield dainties for them; and he that can tell
> What pleasant fruit, yea, leaves, these trees do yield,
> Will soon sell all that he may buy this field.

When they were ready to go on – for they were not yet at the end of their journey – they ate and drank, and then left.

Now I saw in my dream that they had not travelled far before the river and the path diverged for a while. They were not a little sorry to see this, yet they dared not leave the path. Now the path from the river was rough, and their feet were tender as a result of their travels. The pilgrims felt discouraged because of the path (Num. 21:4), and wished it were better. Now not far in front of them, on the left-hand side of the road, there was a meadow, called By-path meadow, and a stile leading into it.

Then Christian said to his companion, 'If this meadow lies alongside our path, let's go over into it.'

He went to the stile to see, and sure enough, a path ran

parallel to theirs on the other side of the fence.

'Just what I was wanting,' Christian said. 'The going will be easier here. Come on, Hopeful, let's go over.'

'But what if this path should lead us out of the way?' Hopeful asked.

'That isn't very likely,' said his friend. 'Look, it runs along by the side of ours.'

So Hopeful, having been persuaded by his companion, went after him over the stile, and together they set off along the path in the field, finding it very easy to walk on. Then, looking ahead, they spotted a man walking as they did (his name was Vain-Confidence). So they called out to him, and asked him where the path led.

'To the Celestial Gate,' he said.

'Look,' said Christian, 'didn't I tell you? That shows we're right.'

So they followed, while he went ahead of them. But night came on, and it grew very dark, so that those behind lost sight of the man in front.

Then Vain-Confidence, who couldn't see the path now, fell into a deep pit (Isa. 9:16), which had been purposely dug there by the prince of those grounds in order to catch overconfident fools. And Vain-Confidence was dashed in pieces by his fall.

Christian and his companion heard the sound of falling and called out to know what was the matter. But there was no answer, only a groaning.

Then Hopeful said, 'Where are we now?'

But Christian was silent, suddenly afraid that he'd led them out of the way. And now it began to rain and thunder, and lightning began to flash in a dreadful way. And the water rose violently.

Then Hopeful groaned and said, 'Oh, if only I'd kept on my path!'

Christian said, 'Who'd have thought that this path would have led us out of the way?'

'From the beginning I was afraid of this,' said Hopeful.

'That's why I gave you that gentle warning. I'd have spoken more plainly, except that you're older than I.'

'Good brother, don't be angry with me. I'm sorry I've led you out of the way, and have brought you into such danger. Please, forgive me, I didn't intend any harm.'

'Don't be upset, brother. I forgive you, and what's more, I believe that this will work out for our good.'

'I am glad I'm with a Christian brother who's so forgiving. But we mustn't stand about. Let's try to go back again.'

'But, good brother, let me go on ahead.'

'No, if you don't mind, let me go first, so that if there is any danger I may be the first to face it, because it's all my fault that we've both left the path.'

'No,' said Hopeful, 'you mustn't go first. You're too upset and may lead us out of the way again.'

Then, to encourage them, they heard a voice saying, 'Take note of the highway, the road that you take. Return . . .' (Jer. 31:21).

By this time the water was very high, so that the way back was dangerous. (As I watched I thought that it's easier going out of the way when we're in it, than going in when we're out.) But they risked the return journey though the night was so dark, and the flood so high that nine or ten times they were on the verge of drowning.

For all their skill, they couldn't make it to the stile that night, so coming at last across a small shelter, they sat down to wait till daybreak. However, overcome by tiredness, they fell asleep.

Now not far from where they were lying there was a castle. It was called Doubting Castle and was owned by Giant Despair and it was in his grounds they were now sleeping. The next morning he got up early and as he was walking up and down in his fields, he caught Christian and Hopeful asleep in his grounds. Grimly he ordered them to wake up and angrily asked where they were from, and what they were doing in his grounds. They told him they were pilgrims and that they had lost their way.

Then the Giant said, 'Last night you trespassed on my property, you trampled on my ground and lay down on it, and therefore you must come along with me.'

So they were forced to go because he was stronger than they were. Also there was nothing they could say, for they knew they were in the wrong. So the Giant drove them in front of him to his castle and threw them into a very dark, nasty and stinking dungeon. Here then they lay from Wednesday morning till Saturday night, without one bit of bread, or one drop of drink. There was no light, and no one to ask how they were. Now their plight was evil indeed for they were far from friends and acquaintances (Ps. 88:18). And in this place Christian's sorrow was doubled because it was through his ill-advised counsel that they had come into this misery.

Now Giant Despair had a wife, and her name was Diffidence. When he was gone to bed he told his wife what he'd done. He said he had taken a couple of prisoners and cast them into his dungeon for trespassing on his grounds. And he asked her what else it would be best to do to them. She asked who they were, where they had come from and where they were bound for, and he told her. Then she advised him that when he got up in the morning he should beat them mercilessly.

So when he got up he armed himself with a deadly crab-tree cudgel, and went down into the dungeon. First he set about berating his prisoners as if they were dogs, although they never uttered one angry word. Then he fell upon them and beat them fearfully, till they were helpless, unable even to turn over on the floor. This done he withdrew, leaving them there to grieve in their misery, and suffer in their distress. All that day passed in sighs and bitter lamentations.

The next night Diffidence again talked with her husband about Christian and Hopeful and hearing that they were still alive, she said, 'Advise them to do away with themselves'.

So when morning came he went to them again, behaving as disagreeably as ever. Seeing that they were very sore from the beating that he'd given them the day before, he told them that since they were never likely to come out of that place the only thing to do was to make an end of themselves at once, either with a knife, by a noose, or poison.

'Why,' he said, 'should you choose life, since it brings so much bitterness?'

But they asked him to let them go.

With that he glared furiously at them and rushing to them would without doubt have finished them off himself, but he fell into one of his fits (for in the hot sun he sometimes had fits, and for a time lost the use of his hands). So he came away, leaving them as before to consider what to do. Then the prisoners talked together about whether or not it was better to take his advice.

'Brother,' Christian said, 'what shall we do? Our life is wretched now. For my part, I don't know whether it's better to live like this, or die out of hand. "I prefer strangling and death, rather than this body of mine" (Job 7:15), and the grave would be more comfortable than this dungeon. Shall we do what the giant says?'

'It's true that our present condition is dreadful, and I find death far more welcome than living like this for ever,' Hopeful said. 'But let's think about it. The Lord of the country to which we're going has said, "You shall not murder". We're forbidden to kill another human being, so how much more are we forbidden to follow the giant's advice and kill ourselves? Besides, to kill another person is merely killing a body but to kill oneself is to kill body and soul at once. And moreover, my brother, you talk of comfort in the grave, but have you forgotten the hell to which murderers certainly go? For "no murderer has eternal life in him" (1 John 3:15). And let's consider again that Giant Despair hasn't taken all the power of the law into his own hands. Others, as far as I can understand, have been captured by him as well, and yet have escaped out of his hands. Who knows but that God, who made the world, may cause that Giant Despair to die? At some time or other he may forget to lock us in, or maybe he'll soon have another of his fits in front of us, and lose the use of his limbs. If that should ever happen again, I'm resolved to act like a man and try my utmost to get away. I was a fool not to try before. But come what may, brother, let's be patient and endure it a while. Time may give us a happy release. Don't let's be our own murderers.'

With these words Hopeful restrained his brother. So that day passed, with the two prisoners lying miserably together in the dark.

Towards evening the Giant went down into the dungeon again to see if his prisoners had followed his advice. He found them alive, but that was all you could say. What with the lack of bread and water, and with the wounds they had received when he beat them, they could do little but breathe. But, as I say, he found them alive, and at this he fell into a furious rage, and told them that since they had disobeyed his counsel it would be worse for them than if they'd never been born.

At this they trembled violently, and I think that Christian fainted. When he had recovered slightly, they renewed their conversation about the Giant's advice, and discussed whether or not they had better take it. Now Christian again seemed to be for doing away with themselves, but Hopeful replied a second time as follows.

'My brother,' he said, 'don't you remember how brave you've been up to now? Apollyon couldn't crush you, nor could anything that you heard or saw or felt in the Valley of the Shadow of Death. Think what hardship, terror, and bewilderment you've already gone through, and after all that are you reduced to a bundle of fears? I'm in the dungeon with you, and I'm a far weaker man by nature than you are. This giant has wounded me as well as you, and has cut off my supply of bread and water, and like you I pine for the light. But let's just exercise a little more patience.

Remember how brave you were at Vanity Fair, and how you were neither afraid of the chain nor the cage, nor even of bloody death. So let us bear up with patience as well as we can, even if only to avoid the shame that it ill becomes a Christian to be found in.'

Now it was night again, and when the Giant and his wife were in bed she asked him about the prisoners, and whether they had taken his advice. He replied, 'They're stubborn rogues, they'd rather bear any hardship than do away with themselves.'

Then she said, 'Tomorrow, take them into the castle-yard, and show them the bones and skulls of those you've already dispatched, and make them believe that before the end of the week you'll tear them to pieces, as you've done to their like before them.'

So when morning came the Giant went to them again, and taking them into the castle-yard he showed them the bones, as his wife had suggested. 'These,' he said, 'were once pilgrims, as you are. They trespassed on my grounds, as you've done, and when I was ready I tore them to pieces, and within ten days I'll do the same to you. Be off! Get down to your cell again.' And with that he beat them all the way there. So all Saturday they lay there in a terrible state, as before.

Now when it was night and when Mrs Diffidence and her husband the Giant were in bed, they began to talk again about their prisoners. The Giant was surprised that neither his blows nor his advice could finish them off.

His wife replied, 'I'm afraid they're living in the hope that someone will come to set them free. Or they've picklocks on them, and hope to escape that way.'

'Do you think so, my dear?' the Giant said. 'I'll search them in the morning.'

Well, about midnight on Saturday Christian and Hopeful began to pray, and continued in prayer till almost daybreak.

A little before it was day Christian, now half beside himself, broke out passionately, 'What a fool I am lying like this in a stinking dungeon when I could be free. I've a key in my breast called Promise and I'm certain it'll open any lock in Doubting Castle.'

Then Hopeful said, 'That's good news, brother, get it out and try.'

Christian pulled it out and tried it at the dungeon door. As he turned the key the lock was released and the door swung open. So Christian and Hopeful both came out. Then Christian went to the outer door that leads into the castle-yard, and the key opened that door, too. After that he went to the iron gate, which also had to be opened. That lock was desperately hard, yet the key eventually turned. They pushed open the gate and quickly escaped. But as it opened that gate creaked so loudly that Giant Despair woke up. He jumped up hastily out of bed to chase his prisoners but felt his limbs go weak as his fits seized him again. So he was unable to go after them.

Christian and Hopeful went on till they came to the King's highway again and there they were safe because they were out of the Giant's jurisdiction.

When they had climbed over the stile they discussed what they could do to stop others who came after from falling into the hands of Giant Despair. After a while they agreed to erect a pillar at the stile, and to engrave this sentence on its side, 'Over this stile lies the way to Doubting Castle, which is kept by Giant Despair. He despises the King of the Celestial Country, and seeks to destroy his holy pilgrims.' Many who followed after them read what was written, and escaped danger.

This done, they sang,

Out of the way we went, and then we found
What 'twas to tread upon forbidden ground:
And let them that come after have a care,
Lest heedlessness makes them as we to fare;
Lest they, for trespassing, his prisoners are,
Whose Castle's Doubting, and whose name's Despair.

The Land of Beulah

Now in my dream I saw that the pilgrims were entering the land of Beulah (Isa. 62:4), where the air was very sweet and pleasant. As the path led through this land they were able to refresh themselves there for a time. There they continually heard the singing of birds, and every day saw the flowers appear on the earth, and heard the cooing of doves (S. of S. 2:12) in the land. In this country the sun shines night and day, for this land is beyond the Valley of the Shadow of Death, and out of the reach of Giant Despair, nor could they as much as see Doubting Castle. They were within sight of the city they were going to, and also met some of its inhabitants, for this land is on the borders of heaven and the Shining Ones frequently walk in it. It was in this land that the contract between the Bride and the Bridegroom was renewed: yes, 'as a bridegroom rejoices over his bride, so will your God rejoice over you' (Isa. 62:5). There they lacked neither corn nor wine, for they found plenty of everything they had looked for in all their pilgrimage. There they heard voices from out of the City – loud voices, saying, 'Say to the Daughter of Zion, "See, your Saviour comes! See, his reward is with him, and his recompense accompanies him"' (Isa. 62:11). And all the inhabitants of the country called them 'the Holy People, the Redeemed of the Lord . . . [the] Sought After' (Isa. 62:12).

As they walked in this land they were far happier than they had been in places more remote from the kingdom to which they were bound, and being closer to the City they had an even finer view of it. It was built of pearls and precious stones, and its streets were paved with gold. When he saw the natural glory of the City, and the reflection of the sun shining on it, Christian fell sick with desire. Hopeful also had several attacks of the same illness. So here they lay for a while, crying out because of their pangs, 'If you find my lover, what will you tell him? Tell him I am faint with love' (S. of S. 5:8).

But at last, feeling a little stronger, and more able to bear their sickness, they continued on their way, and came nearer and nearer to the city. Here there were orchards, vineyards, and gardens with gates which opened straight on to the highway. As they came up to these places they saw the gardener standing on the path. The pilgrims said to him, 'Whose lovely vineyards and gardens are these?'

He answered, 'They are the King's, and are planted here for his own pleasure, and also for the refreshment of pilgrims.'

So the gardener led them into the vineyards, and told them to refresh themselves with the delicious fruit (Deut. 23:24). He also showed them the King's walks and the arbours where he delighted to go, and here they lingered and slept.

Now in my dream I saw that at this time they talked more in their sleep than in all their journey so far. As I was wondering about this the gardener spoke to me. 'Why are you wondering about this? The grapes of these vineyards "goeth down sweetly, causing the lips of them that are asleep to speak"' (S. of S. 7:9 av).

I saw that when they were awake they got ready to go up to the City. But, as I said, the reflection of the sun on the City (for the City was 'of pure gold' [Rev. 21:18]), was so gloriously brilliant that as yet they could not look openly at it, but could only look through an instrument made for that purpose. Then I saw that as they went on they were met by two men. Their clothes shone like gold, and their faces shone like the light (2 Cor. 3:18).

These men asked the pilgrims where they came from, and they told them. They also asked them where they had lodged, and what difficulties and dangers, what encouragements and pleasures, they had met on the way, and they told them. Then the men who met them said, 'You have only two difficulties to overcome, and then you're in the City.'

Christian and his companion asked the men to go along

with them, and they told them that they would. 'But,' they said, 'you must reach the City by your own faith.'

I saw in my dream that they went on together till they came within sight of the gate, but then I saw that between them and the gate there was a river. The river was very deep and there was no bridge over it. At the sight of this river the pilgrims were stunned but the men with them said, 'You must go through, or you cannot come to the gate.'

Death is not welcome to nature, though by it we pass out of this world into glory

The pilgrims then asked if there was no other way to the gate. The men answered, 'Yes, but since the foundation of the world only two people – Enoch and Elijah – have been permitted to tread that path. Nor will anyone else go along it until the last trumpet sounds' (1 Cor. 15:51–2). At this these pilgrims, and especially Christian, began to feel very despondent. They looked this way and that but could find no way to avoid the river. Then they asked the men if the river was the same depth right the way across. They said, 'No, it's not. But this won't help you. You'll find it deeper or shallower according to your trust in the King.'

So they prepared to face the water. As he waded in, Christian began to sink. Crying out to his good friend Hopeful, he said, 'I'm sinking in deep waters; the breakers are going over my head, all the waves are going over me.' Selah.

Then Hopeful said, 'Cheer up, brother; I can feel the bottom, and it's good.'

But Christian called out, 'Oh! my friend, "The sorrows of death have compassed me about." I shall not see the land that flows with milk and honey.' And with that a great darkness and horror fell on Christian so that he was unable to see ahead. Also he lost most of his senses, so that he could neither remember nor talk correctly about any of the sweet encouragements that he had received during his pilgrimage. Everything he said revealed that his mind was full of horror, and his heart full of dread. He was terrified that he would die in that river and never go through the gate. Those who stood watching also saw that he was obsessed by thoughts of the sins that he'd committed, both before and after he had become a pilgrim. From time to time his words revealed that he was also troubled by apparitions of hobgoblins and evil spirits.

Hopeful had great difficulty in keeping his brother's head above water, in fact sometimes Christian went quite under and then after a while would rise up again half dead.

Hopeful tried to comfort him, saying, 'Brother, I can see the gate, and men standing by it to receive us.'

But Christian would answer, 'It's you, it's you they're waiting for, you've been hopeful ever since I've known you.'

'And so have you,' Hopeful said.

'Oh, brother, surely if I were right with God he'd come to help me, but he's brought me into this snare, because of my sins and has left me.'

Then Hopeful said, 'My brother, you've quite forgotten that text about the wicked which says: "They have no struggles; their bodies are healthy and strong. They are free from the burdens common to man; they are not plagued by human ills" (Ps. 73:4–5). The troubles and distresses you're going through are not a sign that God has forsaken you. They're sent to try you, to see whether you'll call to mind all you've experienced up to now of his goodness, and dwell upon him in your distress.'

Then I saw in my dream that Christian was lost in thought for a while. Then Hopeful added these words, 'Be of good cheer, Jesus Christ makes you whole.'

With that Christian broke out with a loud cry, 'Oh, I see him again! And he tells me, "When you pass through the waters, I will be with you; and when you pass through the rivers, they will not sweep over you"' (Isa. 43:2).

Then they both took courage, and after that the enemy

was as still as a stone until they had gone over. Soon Christian found ground to stand on, and after that the rest of the river was only shallow. So they got over.

Now on the bank of the river on the far side they saw the two shining men again, waiting for them. As they came out of the river the men saluted them, and said, 'We are ministering spirits sent to serve those who will inherit salvation' (Heb. 1:14). In this way they went along towards the gate.

Now you must note that the city stood on a great hill. But the pilgrims went up that hill easily because these two men were holding their arms and leading them. Also they had left their earthly clothes behind them in the river, for though they went in wearing them, they came out without them. Therefore they went up quickly and nimbly, though the foundation upon which the city was built was higher than the clouds. So they went up through the regions of the air, talking delightedly as they went, feeling very encouraged because they were over the river, and were accompanied by such glorious companions.

The conversation was about the glory of the place. The Shining Ones told Christian and Hopeful that no words could express its beauty and glory. 'There,' they said, 'is Mount Zion, the heavenly Jerusalem . . . thousands upon thousands of angels . . . the spirits of righteous men made perfect' (Heb. 12:22–23). 'You are going now,' they said, 'to the Paradise of God, where you will see the Tree of Life, and eat its never-fading fruits. And when you arrive white robes will be given you, and every day you will walk and talk with the King, even all the days of eternity (Rev. 2:7; 3:4–5; 22:5). You will never see again the things you saw when you were in the lower regions upon the earth – sorrow, sickness, and death, for the former things are passed away (Isa. 65:16). You are going now to Abraham, to Isaac and Jacob, and to the prophets, men whom God has taken away from the evil to come, and who are now resting on their beds, each one walking in his righteousness' (Isa. 57:1–2).

Christian and Hopeful then asked, 'What must we do in the holy place?'

And they were told, 'There you will receive comfort for all your toil, and joy for all your sorrow. You will reap what you have sown, even the fruit of all your prayers, your tears, and sufferings for the King as you came on your way (Gal. 6:7–8). In that place you will wear crowns of gold, and always enjoy the sight and vision of the Holy One, for there you "shall see him as he is" (1 John 3:2). There also you will serve him continually with praise and shouting and thanksgiving. You will serve the One you longed to serve in the world though you found it so difficult because of the weakness of your flesh. There your eyes will be delighted with seeing, and your ears with hearing the pleasant voice of the Mighty One. There you will enjoy your friends again, who have gone there before you, and there you will receive with joy everyone who follows you into the holy place. There also you will be clothed with glory and majesty, and put into a carriage fit to ride out with the King of Glory. When he comes with sound of the trumpet in the clouds, as upon the wings of the wind, you will come with him, and when he sits upon the throne of judgment you will sit by him. Yes, and when he passes sentence upon all evil-doers, be they angels or men, you will also have a voice in that judgment, because they are his and your enemies. Also, when he again returns to the city, you will go, too, with the sound of trumpet, and be with him for ever' (1 Thess. 4:13–17; Jude 14; Dan. 7:9–10; 1 Cor. 6:2–3).

Now while they were drawing close to the gate, a company of the heavenly host came out to meet them. The two Shining Ones said: 'These are the men who loved our Lord when they were in the world, and have left everything for his holy name. He has sent us to fetch them and we have brought them up to here on their longed-for journey so that they may go in and look at their Redeemer with joy.'

Then the heavenly host gave a great shout, saying, 'Blessed are those who are invited to the wedding supper of the Lamb' (Rev. 19:9). Several of the King's trumpeters also came to meet them, clothed in white and shining garments, and all the heavens echoed to the sound of their melodious notes. These trumpeters greeted Christian and his companion with ten thousand welcomes from the world, saluting them with shouting and trumpet call.

After this the company surrounded them on every side. Some went before, some behind; some on the right hand, and some on the left as if to guard them through the upper regions. As they went the melodious music rang out on high, so that to those watching it was as if heaven itself had come down to meet them. In this way they walked on together, and as they walked every now and then these trumpeters, with joyful notes, with music and looks and gestures, still showed to Christian and his brother how welcome they were in that company, and with what gladness they had come to meet them.

And now it was as if Christian and Hopeful were in heaven before they reached it. They were swallowed up with the sight of angels, and the sound of their melodious notes. All this time they could see the city itself and they thought they could hear all the bells in the city ringing out to welcome them in. But, above all, they were filled with warm and joyful thoughts about how they would live there with such company, for ever and ever. Oh what tongue, or pen, could express their glorious joy! And so in this way they came up to the gate.

Now when they arrived there they saw written over it in letters of gold, the words 'Blessed are those who wash their robes, that they may have right to the tree of life, and may go through the gates into the city' (Rev 22:14).

Then in my dream I saw that the shining men bade them call at the gate. When they had done this some from above looked over the gate — Enoch, Moses, and Elijah, with others. They were told 'These pilgrims have come from the city of Destruction, because of their love for the King of this place.'

And then each pilgrim gave in the certificate which he had received at the beginning. These were carried to the King, who, when he had read them, said, 'Where are the men?'

He was told, 'They are standing outside the gate.'

'Open the gates,' commanded the King, 'that the right-eous nation may enter, the nation that keeps faith' (Isa. 26:2).

Now in my dream I saw that these two men went in at the gate. And behold, as they entered, they were trans-figured, and garments were put on them that shone like gold. Others met them with harps and crowns, which they gave to them. The harps were for praise, the crowns were in token of honour. Then I heard in my dream that all the bells in the city rang out again for joy, and the pilgrims were told, 'Come and share your master's happiness!' (Matt. 25:21).

I also heard Christian and Hopeful singing aloud and saying, 'To him who sits on the throne and to the Lamb be praise and honour and glory and power, for ever and ever!' (Rev. 5:13).

Just as the gates were opened to let in the men, I looked in after them. The city shone like the sun, the streets were paved with gold, and in the streets walked many men with crowns on their heads, palms in their hands, and golden harps with which to sing praises.

Some had wings, and they spoke to one another saying, 'Holy, holy, holy, is the Lord!'

After that they shut the gates. And I was outside, wish-ing I were among them.

Now while I was gazing at all these things I turned my head to look back, and saw Ignorance come up to the riverside. He got over quickly and without half the diffi-culty which the other two had experienced, for as it hap-pened a ferryman, called Vain-hope had come, and with his boat had helped him over. So Ignorance, like the others, climbed the hill to come up to the gate, only he came alone, and no one met him with the least encouragement. When he arrived at the gate he looked up to the writing that was above it and then began to knock, supposing that he would be quickly admitted. But the man who looked over the top of the gate asked him, 'Where are you from and what do you want?'

He answered, 'I've eaten and drunk in the presence of the King, and he has taught in our streets.'

Then they asked him for his certificate so that they might go and show it to the King. He fumbled in his clothes for one, and found none.

Then said they, 'Haven't you got one?' But the man was silent. So they told the King, but he wouldn't come down to see him. Instead he commanded the two shining ones who had conducted Christian and Hopeful to the City, to go out and take Ignorance, and bind him hand and foot, and lead him away. They took him up, and carried him through the air to a door in the side of the hill, and put him there. Then I saw that there was a way to hell even from the gates of heaven, as well as from the City of Destruction. So I awoke, and saw it was a dream.

Conclusion

Now, reader, I have told my dream to thee,
See if thou canst interpret it to me,
Or to thyself, or neighbour: but take heed
Of misinterpreting; for that, instead
Of doing good, will but thyself abuse:
By misinterpreting, evil ensues.

Take heed also that thou be not extreme
In playing with the outside of my dream;
Nor let my figure or similitude
Put thee into a laughter or a feud.

Leave this for boys and fools; but as for thee,
Do thou the substance of my matter see.

Put by the curtains, look within the veil,
Turn up my metaphors, and do not fail.
There, if thou seekest them, such things thou'lt find
As will be helpful to an honest mind.

What of my dross thou findest there, be bold
To throw away, but yet preserve the gold.
What if my gold be wrapped up in ore?
None throws away the apple for the core;
But if thou shalt cast all away as vain,
I know not but 'twill make me dream again.

3

A Relation of the Imprisonment of Mr John Bunyan

[The original title page was printed as follows: *A Relation of the imprisonment of Mr John Bunyan, minister of the Gospel at Bedford, in November 1660. His examination before the Justices, his conference with the Clerk of the Peace, what passed between the Judges and his wife, when she presented a petition for his deliverance. Written by himself, and never before published.*

'Blessed are ye which are persecuted for righteousness sake, for theirs is the kingdom of heaven.

'Blessed are ye when men shall revile you and persecute you, and shall say all manner of evil against you falsely for my name's sake.

'Rejoice and be exceeding glad, for great is your reward in heaven, for so persecuted they the prophets which were before you.' (*Matthew 5:10–11*).

London: Printed for James Buckland, at the Buck, in Paternoster-Row, MDCCLXV (1765)]

(The Relation of my Imprisonment in the month of November, 1660, when, by the good hand of my God, I had for five or six years together, without any great interruption, freely preached the blessed Gospel of our Lord

Jesus Christ; and had also, through his blessed grace, some
encouragement by his blessings thereupon: The devil, that
old enemy of man's salvation, took his opportunity to
inflame the hearts of his vassals against me, insomuch that
at the last, I was laid out for by the warrant of a justice, and
was taken and committed to prison. The relation thereof is
as follows:)

Upon the 12th of this instant November, 1660, I was
desired by some friends in the country to come to teach at
Samsell, by Harlington, in Bedfordshire; to whom I made
a promise, if the Lord permitted, to be with them on the
time aforesaid. The Justice hearing thereof, whose name is
Mr Francis Wingate, forthwith issued out his warrant to
take me and bring me before him, and in the meantime to
keep a very strong watch about the house where the meeting should be kept, as if we that were to meet together in
that place did intend to do some fearful business to the
destruction of the country; when, alas, the constable, when
he came in, found us only with our Bibles in our hands,
ready to speak and hear the word of God; for we were just
about to begin our exercise. Nay, we had begun in prayer
for the blessing of God upon our opportunity, intending
to have preached the word of the Lord unto them there
present; but the constable coming in prevented us, so that
I was taken and forced to depart the room.

But had I been minded to have played the coward, I
could have escaped and kept out of his hands. For when I
was come to my friend's house, there was whispering that
that day I should be taken, for there was a warrant to take
me. Which when my friend heard, he being somewhat
timorous, questioned whether we had best have our meeting or not; and whether it might not be better for me to
depart, lest they should take me and have me before the
Justice and after that send me to prison; for he knew
better than I what spirit they were of, living near them. To
whom I said, 'No, by no means. I will not stir; neither will I

have the meeting dismissed for this. Come, be of good cheer! Let us not be daunted; our cause is good; we need not be ashamed of it. To preach God's word is so good a work, that we shall be well rewarded if we suffer for that.'

After this I walked into the close, where (I considering the matter somewhat seriously) this came into my mind — that I had showed myself hearty and courageous in my preaching and had, blessed be grace, made it my business to encourage others; therefore, I thought, if I should now run and make an escape, it will be of a very ill savour in the country: for what will my weak and newly-converted brethren think of it but that I was not so strong in deed as I was in word?

I also feared that if I should run now there was a warrant out for me, I might by so doing make them afraid to stand, when great words only should be spoken to them. Besides, I thought, that seeing God's mercy should choose me to go on the forlorn hope in this country; that is, to be first, that should be opposed, for the gospel. If I fled, it might be a discouragement to the whole body who might follow after me. And further, I thought the world thereby would take occasion at my cowardliness, to have blasphemed the gospel, and to have had some ground to suspect worse of me and my profession than I deserved.

These things with others considered by me, I came in again to the house, with a full resolution to keep the meeting and not to go away; though I could have been gone about an hour before the officer apprehended me. But I would not, for I was resolved to see the utmost of what they could say or do to me. For, blessed be the Lord, I knew of no evil that I had done or said.

And so, as aforesaid, I began the meeting; but being prevented by the constable's coming in with his warrant to take me, I could not proceed. But before I went away I spake some few words of counsel and encouragement to the people. The constable and the Justice's man waiting on us would not be at quiet till they had me away and that we

departed to the house. But because the Justice was not at
home that day, there was a friend of mine engaged for me
to bring me to the constable on the next morning. Otherwise the constable must have charged a watch with me or
have secured me some other way, as my crime was so great.

Before the Justice

So on the next morning we went to the constable, and so to
the Justice [Justice Wingate]. He asked the constable what
we did, where we were met together and what we had with
us. I trow he meant whether we had armour or not; but
when the constable told him that there were only met a few
of us together to preach and hear the word, and no sign of
anything else, he could not well tell what to say; yet
because he had sent for me, he did venture to put out a
few proposals to me, which were to this effect, namely —
what I did there, and why I did not content myself with
following my calling, for it was against the law that such as
I should be admitted to do as I did.

To which I answered, that the intent of my coming
thither, and to other places, was to instruct and counsel
people to forsake their sins and close in with Christ, lest
they did miserably perish; and that I could do both these
without confusion, to wit, follow my calling, and preach
the word also.

To which words he was in a chafe, as it appeared; for he
said that he would break the neck of our meetings.

I said, 'It may be so'. Then he wished me to get sureties
to be bound for me, or else he would send me to the jail.
My sureties being ready, I called them in. And when the
bond for my appearance was made, he told them that they
were bound to keep me from preaching; and that if I did
preach their bonds would be forfeited. To which I
answered, that then I should break them; for I should not
leave speaking the word of God: even to counsel, comfort,
exhort, and teach the people among whom I came; and I

thought this to be a work that had no hurt in it, but was rather worthy of commendation than blame.

Whereat he told me that if they would not be so bound, my mittimus must be made, and I sent to the jail, there to lie to the quarter-sessions.

Now while my mittimus was being made, the Justice was withdrawn, and in comes an old enemy of the truth, Dr Lindale, who, when he was come in, fell to taunting me with many reviling terms.

To whom I answered, that I did not come thither to talk with him, but with the justice. Whereat he supposing that I had nothing to say for myself, triumphed as if he had got the victory, condemning me for meddling with that for which I could show no warrant. And asked me if I had taken the oaths, and if I had not, that it was a pity but that I should be sent to prison.

I told him that if I minded, I could answer to any sober question that he should put to me. He then urged me again, how I could prove it lawful for me to preach, with a great deal of confidence and victory.

But, at last, because he should see that I could answer him if I listed, I cited to him Peter, who said, 'As every man hath received the gift, even so let him minister the same.'

'Aye,' saith he, 'to whom is that spoken?'

'To whom?' I said. 'Why, to every man who has received a gift from God. Mark, saith the apostle, "As every man that received a gift from God." And again, "You may all prophesy one by one."' Whereat the man was a little stopped, and went a softer pace. But, as he was unwilling to lose the day, he said:

'Indeed I do remember that I have read of one Alexander, a Coppersmith [2 Timothy 4:14], who did much oppose, and disturb the apostles.'

To which I answered that I also had read of very many priests and pharisees that had their hands in the blood of our Lord Jesus Christ.

'Aye,' saith he, 'and you are one of those scribes and

pharisees, for you, with a pretence, make long prayers to devour widows' houses.'

I answered that if he got no more by preaching and praying than I had done, he would not be so rich as now he was. But that Scripture coming into my mind, 'Answer not a fool according to his folly,' I was as sparing of my speech as I could, without prejudice to truth.

Now by this time my mittimus was made, and I committed to the constable to be sent to the jail in Beford.

But as I was going, two of my brethren met with me by the way, and desired the constable to stay, supposing that they should prevail with the justice, through the favour of a pretended friend, to let me go at liberty. So we did stay, while they went to the justice, and after much discourse with him, it came to this; that if I would come to him again, and say some certain words to him, I should be released. Which when they told me, I said if the words were such that might be said with a good conscience, I should, or else I should not. So through their importunity I went back again, but not believing that I should be delivered. For I feared their spirit was too full of opposition to the truth to let me go, unless I should in something or other dishonour my God, and wound my conscience. Wherefore as I went, I lifted up my heart to God, for light, and strength, to be kept, that I might not do any thing that might either dishonour him, or wrong my won soul, or be a grief or discouragement to any that was inclining after the Lord Jesus Christ.

Well, when I came to the justice again, there was Mr Foster of Bedford, who coming out of another room, and seeing of me by the light of the candle, for it was dark night when I went thither, he said to me, 'Who is there, John Bunyan?' With such seeming affection, as if he would have leaped on my neck and kissed me, which made me somewhat wonder, that such a man as he, with whom I had so little acquaintance, and besides, that had ever been a close opposer of the ways of God, should carry himself so full of love to me. But, afterwards, when I saw what he did, it caused me to remember those sayings, 'Their tongues are smoother than oil, but their words are drawn swords.' And again, 'Beware of men.' When I answered him that blessed be God I was well, then he said, 'What is the occasion of your being here?' To whom I answered that I was at a meeting of people a little way off, intending to speak a word of exhortation to them; the justice hearing thereof, said I, was pleased to send his warrant, to fetch me before him.

'So,' said he, 'I understand. But, well, if you will promise to call the people no more together, you shall have your liberty to go home. For my brother [William Foster was brother-in-law to Justice Wingate] is very loath to send you to prison, if you will be but ruled.'

'Sir,' said I, 'pray what do you mean by calling the people together? My business is not anything among them when they are come together but to exhort them to look after the salvation of their souls, that they may be saved.'

Saith he, 'We must not enter into explication, or dispute now; but if you will say you will call the people no more together, you may have your liberty; if not, you must be sent away to prison.'

'Sir,' said I, 'I shall not force or compel any man to hear me, but yet if I come into any place where there is a people met together, I should, according to the best of my skill and wisdom, exhort and counsel them to seek out after the Lord Jesus Christ, for the salvation of their souls.'

He said that was none of my work. I must follow my calling, and if I would but leave off preaching, and follow my calling, I should have the justice's favour, and be acquitted presently.

To whom I said that I could follow my calling and that too, namely, preaching the word. And I did look upon it as my duty to do them both, as I had an opportunity.

He said to have any such meetings was against the law; and therefore he would have me leave off, and say I would call the people no more together.

To whom I said that I durst not make any further promise. For my conscience would not suffer me to do it. And again, I did look upon it as my duty to do as much good as I could, not only in my trade, but also in communicating to all people wheresoever I came, the best knowledge I had in the word.

He told me that I was the nearest the Papists of any, and that he would convince me immediately.

I asked him wherein.

He said, in that we understood the Scriptures literally.

I told him, that those which were to be understood literally we understood so; but for those that was to be understood otherwise, we endeavoured so to understand them.

He said, 'Which of the Scriptures do you understand literally?'

I said, 'This: "He that believes shall be saved." This was to be understood, just as it was spoken, that whoever believeth in Christ, shall, according to the plain and simple words of the text, be saved.'

He said that I was ignorant, and did not understand the Scriptures; for, said he, 'Can you understand them, when you know not the original Greek?'

To whom I said that if that was his opinion, that no one could understand the Scriptures but those who had the original Greek, then only a very few of the poorest sort should be saved, which was harsh. But the Scripture says that 'God hides his things from the wise and prudent,' that is from the learned of the world, 'and reveals them to babes and sucklings'.

He said there was none that heard me but a company of foolish people.

I told him that there was the wise as well as the foolish that do hear me, and again, those who are most commonly counted foolish by the world are the wisest before God. Also that God had rejected the wise, and mighty and noble, and chosen the foolish, and the base.

He told me that I made people neglect their calling; and that God had commanded people to work six days, and serve him on the seventh.

I told him, that it was the people's duty, both rich and poor, to look out for their souls on those days, as well as for their bodies. And that God would have his people exhort one another daily, while it is called today.

He said again, that there was no one but a company of poor, simple, ignorant people who came to hear me.

I told him, that the foolish and the ignorant had most need of teaching and information, and therefore it would be profitable for me to go on in that work.

'Well,' said he, 'to conclude, but will you promise that you will not call the people together any more? Then you may be released, and go home.'

I told him that I durst say no more than I had said. For I durst not leave off that work which God had called me to.

So he withdrew from me, and then came several of the Justice's servants to me, and told me that I stood so much upon a nicety. The Justice, the servants said, was willing to let me go; and if I would but say I would call the people no more together, I might have my liberty.

I told them, there were more ways than one, in which a man might be said to call the people together. As for instance, if a man get upon the market-place, and there read a book, or the like, though he do not say to the people, 'Sirs, come hither and hear'; yet if they come to him because he reads, he, by his very reading, may be said to call them together; because they would not have been there to hear, if he had not been there to read. And seeing this might be termed a calling the people together, I durst not say I would not call them together; for then, by the same argument, my preaching might be said to call them together.

Then came the Justice and Mr Foster to me again. They saw that I would not be moved or persuaded. Mr Foster told the justice that he must send me away to prison. Thus we parted. Verily, as I was going out of the doors, I had much ado to forbear saying to them that I carried the peace of God along with me. But I held my peace and, blessed be the Lord, went away to prison with God's comfort in my poor soul.

After I had lain in the jail five or six days, the brethren sought means again to get me out of my bondage, for so said my mittimus, that I should lie there until I could find sureties. They went to the justice at Elstow, one Mr Crumpton, to ask him to take bond for my appearing at the quarter-sessions. At the first he told them he would, but afterwards he made a demur at the business, and desired first to see my mittimus, which ran to this purpose. It stated that I went about several conventicles in this country, to the great disparagement of the governement of the church of England. When he had seen it, he said that there might be something more against me than was expressed in my mittimus. And that he was but a young man, therefore he dare not do it. This my jailor told me. Whereat I was not at all daunted, but rather glad, and saw evidently that the Lord had heard me, for before I went down to the justice, I begged God, that if I might do more good by being at liberty than in prison, that then I might be set at liberty. But if not, his will be done, for I was not altogether without hopes but that my imprisonment might be an awakening to the saints in the country, therefore I could not tell well which to choose. Only I in that matter did commit the thing to God. And verily on my return, I did meet my God sweetly in the prison again, comforting me and satisfying me that it was his will and mind that I should be there.

When I came back again to prison, as I was musing at the slender answer of the Justice, this word dropped on my heart with some life, 'For he knew that for envy they had delivered him'.

Thus have I in short declared the manner and the occasion of my being in prison; where I lie waiting the good will of God, to do with me as he pleases. I know that not one hair from my head can fall to the ground without the will of my Father who is in heaven. Let the rage and malice of men be never so great, they can do no more, nor go no further than God permits them. But when they have done their worst, we know all things shall work together for good to those who love God.

Farewell.

Quarter-Sessions

Here is the sum of my examination before Justice Keeling, Justice Chester, Justice Blundale, Justice Beecher, and Justice Snagg.

After I had lain in prison above seven weeks, the quarter-sessions was to be kept in Bradford, for the country thereof; unto which I was to be brought, and when my jailor had set me before those justices, there was a bill of indictment preferred against me. The extent thereof was as follows:

> That John Bunyan of the town of Bedford, labourer, being a person of such and such conditions, has, since such a time, devilishly and perniciously abstained from coming to church to hear divine service, and is a common upholder of several unlawful meetings and conventicles, to the great disturbance and distraction of the good subjects of this kingdom, contrary to the laws of our sovereign lord the king.

When this was read, the clerk of the sessions said unto me, 'What say you to this?'

I said, that as to the first part of it, I was a common frequenter of the church of God. And was also, by grace, a member with those people over whom Christ is the head.

'But,' saith Justice Keeling, who was the judge in that court, 'do you come to church, you know what I mean, to the parish church, to hear the divine service?'

I answered, no, I did not.

He asked me, 'Why?'

I said, because I did not find it commanded in the word of God.

He said we were commanded to pray.

I said, 'But not by the Common Prayer-Book.'

He said, 'How then?'

I said, 'With the spirit. As the apostle says, "I will pray with the spirit and with understanding"' (1 Corinthians 14:15).

He said we might pray with the spirit, and with understanding, and with the Common Prayer-Book also.

I said that those prayers in the Common Prayer-book were made by other men, and not by the work of the Holy Spirit within our hearts. And the apostle says he will pray with the spirit and with understanding, not with the spirit and the Common Prayer-book.

Another justice asked, 'What do you count prayer? Do you think it is to say a few words over before, or among a people?'

I said, 'No, not so. For men might have many elegant, or excellent words, and yet not pray at all. But when a man prays, he does, through a sense of those things which he lacks, which sense is given by the Spirit, pour out his heart before God through Christ. Even though his words may not be many, they are as excellent as others.'

They said that was true.

I said this might be done without the Common Prayer-book.

One of them said, I think it was Justice Blundale, or Justice Snagg, 'How should we know that you do not write out your prayers first, and then read them afterwards to the people?' This he spake in a laughing way.

I said, 'It is not our use, to take a pen and paper and write a few words thereon, and then go and read it over to a company of people.'

'But how should we know it?' said he.

'Sir, it is none of our custom,' said I.

'But,' said Justice Keeling, 'it is lawful to use Common Prayer, and such like forms. For Christ taught his disciples to pray, as John also taught his disciples. And further,' said he, 'cannot one man teach another to pray? Faith comes by hearing. And one man may convince another of sin, and therefore prayers made by men, and read over, are good to teach, and help men to pray.'

While he was speaking these words, God brought that word into my mind Romans chapter 8, verse 26. I say God brought it, for I thought not on it before, but as he was speaking, it came so fresh into my mind, and was set so evidently before me, as if the Scripture had said, 'Take me'; so when he had done speaking:

I said, 'Sir, the Scripture says, that it is the spirit as helpeth our infirmities; for we know not what we should pray for as we ought. But the Spirit itself makes intercession for us, with sighs and groanings which cannot be uttered. Mark, said I, it does not say the Common Prayer-book teaches us how to pray, but the Spirit. And it is the Spirit that helpeth our infirmitites, said the apostle. He does not say it is the Common Prayer-book.

'And as for the Lord's Prayer, although it is an easy thing to say "Our Father" etc. with the mouth, yet there are very few who can, in the spirit, say the first two words of that prayer: that is, who can call God their Father, knowing what it is to be born again, and experience that they are born of the Spirit of God, which if they do not, everything is but babbling.'

Justice Keeling said that that was a truth.

'And I say further, as to your saying that one man may convince another of sin, and that faith comes by hearing, and that one may tell another how he should pray, etc. I say men may tell each other of their sins, but it is the Spirit that must convict them. And although it is said that "faith comes by hearing," yet it is the Spirit that worketh faith in the heart through hearing, or else "they are not profited by hearing" (Hebrews 4:2).

'And though one Man may tell another how he should pray, yet, he cannot pray, nor make his condition known to God, unless the Spirit helps. It is not the Common Prayer-book that can do this. It is the "Spirit that sheweth us our sins" (Matthew 3:16–17), and the "Spirit that sheweth us a Saviour" (John 15:16). And the Spirit that stirreth up in our hearts desires to come to God, for such things as we stand in need of, even sighing out our souls unto him for them with "groans which cannot be uttered".' At this they were rebuffed.

'But,' says Justice Keeling, 'what have you against the Common Prayer-book?'

I said, 'Sir, if you will hear me, I shall lay down my reasons against it.'

He said I should have liberty. 'But first,' said he, 'let me give you one caution. Take heed of speaking irreverently of the Common Prayer-book. For if you do so, you will bring great damage upon yourself.'

So I proceeded, and said my first reason was because it was not commanded in the word of God, and therefore I could not do it.

One of them said, 'Where do you find it commanded in the Scripture, that you should go to Elstow, or Bedford? And yet it is lawful to go to either of them, is it not?'

I said, to go to Elstow or Bedford, was a civil thing, and not material, though not commanded, and yet God's word allowed me to go about my calling, and therefore if it lay there, then to go thither. But to pray was a great part of the divine worship of God, and therefore it ought to be done according to the rule of God's word.

One of them said, 'He will do harm, let him speak no further.'

Justice Keeling said, 'No, no never fear him, we are better established than he is. He can do no harm, we know the Common Prayer-book has been ever since the apostles' time, and it is lawful to be used in the church.'

I said, 'Show me the place in the epistles, where the Common Prayer-book is written, or one text of Scripture that commands me to read it, and I will use it. But yet, notwithstanding,' said I, 'they that have a mind to use it, they have their liberty. I do not wish to stop them, but as for us, we can pray to God without it. Blessed be his name.'

With that one of them said, 'Who is your God? Beelzebub?' Moreover, they often said that I was possessed with the spirit of delusion, and of the devil. I passed over all these sayings. The Lord forgive them. And further, I said, 'Blessed be the Lord for it, we are encouraged to meet together, and to pray, and exhort one another; for we have had the comfortable presence of God among us, for ever blessed be his holy name.'

Justice Keeling called this pedlar's French, saying that I must leave off my canting. The Lord open his eyes!

I said that I would prove that it was lawful for me, and such as I am, to preach the word of God.

He said unto me, 'By what Scripture?'

I said, 'In 1 Peter 4:11, and Acts chapter 18, with other Scriptures,' which he would not allow me to mention but said, 'Hold; not so many, which is the first?'

I said, 'This: "As every man hath receiveth the gift, even so let him minister the same unto another, as good stewards of the manifold grace of God: If any man speak, let him speak as the oracles of God."'

He said, 'Let me a little open that Scripture to you. "As every man hath received the gift", that is,' said he, 'as every man hath received a trade, so let him follow it. If any man has received a gift of tinkering, as you have, let him follow his tinkering. And so other men their trades. And the divine his calling.'

'No, sir,' said I, 'but it is most clear that the apostle speaks here about preaching the word. If you will but compare the verses with each other, the next verse explains this gift, saying, "If any man speak, let him speak as the oracles of God." So that is plain, the Holy Ghost does not so much here exhort civil callings, but the exercising of those gifts that we have received from God.' I would have gone on, but he would not give me leave.

He said we might do it in our families but not otherwise.

I said, if it was lawful to do good to some, it was lawful to do good to more. If it was a good duty to exhort our families, it is good to exhort others. But if they held it a sin to meet together to seek God's face, and to exhort one another to follow Christ, I should sin still, for so we should do.

He said he was not so well versed in Scripture as to dispute. He said, moreover, that they could not wait upon me any longer, but said to me, 'Then you confess the indictment, do you not?' Now, and not till now, I saw I was indicted.

I said, 'This I confess, we have had many meetings together, both to pray to God, and to exhort one another, and that we had the sweet comforting presence of the Lord among us for our encouragement, blessed be his name therefore.' I confessed myself guilty no otherwise.

'Then,' said he, 'hear your judgment. You must be had back again to prison, and there lie for three months following; at the end of three months, if you do not submit to go to church to hear divine service, and leave your preaching, you must be banished from the realm. And if, after such a day as shall be appointed you to be gone, you shall be found in the realm, or found to come over again without special licence from the king, you must stretch by the neck for it, I tell you plainly.' And so he bid my jailor have me away.

I told him, as to this matter, I was at the point with him. For if I was out of prison today, I would preach the gospel again tomorrow, by God's help.

To which one made me some answer: But my jailor pulling me away to be gone, I could not tell what he said.

Thus I departed from them. I can truly say, I bless the

Lord Jesus Christ for it, that my heart was sweetly refreshed in the time of my examination, and also afterwards, at my returning to the prison. So I found Christ's words more than bare trifles, where he said, he 'will give a mouth and wisdom, even such as all the adversaries shall not resist, or gainsay.' And that his peace no man can take from us.

Thus have I given you the substance of my examination. The Lord make these profitable to all that shall read or hear them.

Farewell.

4

The Pilgrim's Progress (Part II)

The author's way of sending forth his second part of The Pilgrim

Go now, my little book, to every place
Where my first pilgrim has but shown his face;
Call at their door: if any say, 'Who's there?'
Then answer thou, 'Christiana is here.'
If they bid thee come in, then enter thou
With all thy joys; and then, as thou know'st how,
Tell who they are, also from whence they came:
Perhaps they'll know them by their looks or name;
But if they should not, ask them yet again
If formerly they did not entertain
One Christian, a pilgrim. If they say
They did, and were delighted in his way,
Then let them know that those related were
Unto him, yea, his wife and children are.
    Tell them that they have left their house and home,
And turned pilgrims, seek a world to come;
That they *have* met with hardships in the way,
That they *do* meet with troubles night and day;
That they have trod on serpents, fought with devils,
Have also overcome a many evils.

Yea, tell them also of the rest, who have,
Of love to pilgrimage, been stout and brave
Defenders of that way, and how they still
Refuse this world, to do their Father's will.
      Go, tell them also of those dainty things
That pilgrimage unto the pilgrim brings.
Let them acquainted be, too, how they are
Beloved of their King, under his care;
What goodly mansions for them he provides;
Though they meet with rough winds and swelling tides,
How brave a calm they will enjoy at last,
Who to their Lord and by his ways hold fast.
      Perhaps with heart and hand they will embrace
Thee, as they did my firstling, and will grace
Thee and thy fellows with such cheer and fair
As shew will, they of pilgrims lovers are.

FIRST OBJECTION

But how, if they will not believe of me
That I am truly thine? 'cause some there be
That counterfeit the pilgrim and his name;
Seek by disguise to seem the very same;
And by that means have wrought themselves into
The hands and houses of I know not who.

ANSWER

'Tis true, some have of late, to counterfeit
My Pilgrim, to their own my title set;
Yea, others half my name and title too
Have stitched to their book, to make them do.
But yet they by their features do declare
Themselves not mine to be, whose'er they are.
      If such thou meet'st with, then thine only way,
Before them all, is, to say out thy say
In thine own native language, which no man
Now useth nor with ease dissemble can.
      If, after all, they still of you shall doubt,

Thinking that you, like gipsies, go about
In naughty wise the country to defile,
Or that you seek good people to beguile
With things unwarrantable: send for me,
And I will testify you pilgrims be;
Yea, I will testify that only you
My pilgrims are; and that alone will do.

SECOND OBJECTION

But yet, perhaps, I may inquire for him
Of those that wish him damned life and limb.
What shall I do, when I at such a door
For pilgrims ask, and they shall rage the more?

ANSWER

Fright not thyself, my book; for such bugbears
Are nothing else but ground for groundless fears.
My Pilgrim's book has travell'd sea and land;
Yet could I never come to understand
That it was slighted or turn'd out of door
By any kingdom, were they rich or poor.
    In France and Flanders, where men kill each other,
My Pilgrim is esteem'd a friend, a brother.
    In Holland too 'tis said, as I am told,
My Pilgrim is with some worth more than gold.
    Highlanders and wild Irish can agree,
My Pilgrim should familiar with them be.
    'Tis in New England under such advance,
Receives there so much loving countenance,
As to be trimm'd, new-cloth'd, and deck'd with gems,
That it might show its features and its limbs;
Yet more, so comely doth my Pilgrim walk,
That of him thousands daily sing and talk.
    If you draw nearer home, it will appear
My Pilgrim knows no ground of shame or fear;
City and country will him entertain
With 'Welcome, Pilgrim.' Yea, they can't refrain

From smiling if my Pilgrim be but by,
Or shews his head in any company.
  Brave gallants do my Pilgrim hug and love,
Esteem it much; yea, value it above
Things of a greater bulk; yea, with delight,
Say my lark's leg is better than a kite.
  Young ladies, and young gentlewomen too,
Do no small kindness to my Pilgrim show;
Their cabinets, their bosoms, and their hearts
My Pilgrim has, 'cause he to them imparts
His pretty riddles in such wholesome strains,
As yields them profit double to their pains
Of reading. Yea, I think I may be bold
To say, some prize him far above their gold.
  The very children that do walk the street,
If they do but my holy Pilgrim meet,
Salute him will, will wish him well, and say,
He is the only stripling of the day.
  They that have never seen him, yet admire
What they have heard of him, and much desire
To have his company, and hear him tell
Those pilgrim stories which he knows so well.
  Yea, some who did not love him at the first,
But call'd him 'Fool' and 'Noddy', say they must,
Now they have seen and heard him, him commend;
And to those whom they love they do him send.
  Wherefore, my Second Part, thou needst not be
Afraid to show thy head; none can hurt thee
That wish but well to him that went before,
'Cause thou com'st after with a second store
Of things as good, as rich, as profitable
For young, for old, for stagg'ring, and for stable.

THIRD OBJECTION

But some there be that say he laughs too loud;
And some do say his head is in a cloud:
Some say, his words and stories are so dark,

They know not how by them to find his mark.

One may, I think, say, 'Both his laughs and cries
May well be guess'd at by his watery eyes.'
Some things are of that nature as to make
One's fancy chuckle while his heart doth ache.
When Jacob saw his Rachel with the sheep,
He did at the same time both kiss and weep.

  Whereas some say a cloud is in his head,
That doth but show how wisdom's covered
With its own mantles; and to stir the mind
To search afer what it fain would find,
Things that seem to be hid in words obscure
Do but the godly mind the more allure
To study what those sayings should contain
That speak to us in such a cloudy strain.

  I also know a dark similitude
Will on the fancy more itself intrude,
And will stick faster in the heart and head,
Than things from similes not borrowed.

  Wherefore, my book, let no discouragement
Hinder thy travels. Behold, thou art sent
To friends, not foes; to friends that will give place
To thee, thy pilgrims and thy words embrace.

  Besides, what my first Pilgrim left conceal'd,
Thou, my brave second Pilgrim, hast reveal'd;
What Christian left lock'd up and went his way,
Sweet Christiana opens with her key.

But some love not the method of your first;
Romance they count it, throw't away as dust.
If I should meet with such, what should I say?
Must I slight them as they slight me, or nay?

ANSWER

My Christiana, if with such thou meet,
By all means in all loving wise them greet;
Render them not reviling for revile;
But if they frown, I prithee on them smile.
Perhaps 'tis nature, or some ill report,
Has made them thus despise, or thus retort.
　　Some love no cheese, some love no fish, and some
Love not their friends, nor their own house or home;
Some start at pig, slight chicken, love not fowl
More than they love a cuckoo or an owl.
Leave such, my Christiana, to their choice,
And seek those who to find thee will rejoice.
By no means strive, but in all humble wise
Present thee to them in thy pilgrim's guise.
　　Go then, my little book, and show to all
That entertain and bid thee welcome shall,
What thou shalt keep close shut up from the rest;
And wish what thou shalt show them may be bless'd
To them for good, may make them choose to be
Pilgrims better by far than thee or me.
　　Go then, I say, tell all men who thou art;
Say, 'I am Christiana, and my part
Is now, with my four sons, to tell you what
It is for men to take a pilgrim's lot.'
　　Go also tell them who and what they be,
That now do go on pilgrimage with thee.
Say, 'Here's my neighbour Mercy; she is one
That has long time with me a pilgrim gone;
Come, see her in her virgin face, and learn
'Twixt idle ones and pilgrims to discern:
Yea, let young damsels learn of her to prize
The world which is to come in any wise.
When little tripping maidens follow God,
And leave old doting sinners to his rod,
'Tis like those days wherein the young ones cried

Hosannah to whom old ones deride.'
   Next tell them of old Honest, who you found,
With his white hairs, treading the pilgrim's ground;
Yea, tell them how plain-hearted this man was,
How after his good Lord he bare his cross.
Perhaps with some grey head this may prevail
With Christ to fall in love, and sin bewail.
   Tell them also how Master Fearing went
On pilgrimage, and how the time he spent
In solitariness, with fears and cries,
And how at last he won the joyful prize.
He *was* a good man, though much down in spirit;
He *is* a good man, and doth life inherit.
   Tell them of Master Feeblemind also,
Who not before, but still behind would go;
Show them also how he had like been slain,
And how one Greatheart did his life regain.
This man was true of heart, though weak in grace;
One might true godliness read in his face.
   Then tell them of Master Ready-to-halt,
A man with crutches, but much without fault;
Tell them how Master Feeblemind and he
Did love, and in opinions much agree;
And let all know, though weakness was their chance,
Yet sometimes one could sing, the other dance.
   Forget not Master Valiant-for-the-Truth,
That man of courage, though a very youth.
Tell every one his spirit was so stout,
No man could ever make him face about;
And how Greatheart and he could not forbear
But put down Doubting Castle, slay Despair.
   Overlook not Master Despondency,
Nor Much-afraid, his daughter, though they lie
Under such mantles as may make them look
With some as if their God had them forsook.
They softly went, but sure; and at the end
Found that the Lord of pilgrims was their Friend.

When thou hast told the world of all these things,
Then turn about, my book, and touch these strings;
Which, if but touched, will such music make,
They'll make a cripple dance, a giant quake.
    Those riddles that lie couch'd within thy breast,
Freely propound, expound; and for the rest
Of thy mysterious lines, let them remain
For those whose nimble fancies shall them gain.
    Now may this little book a blessing be
To those that love this little book and me;
And may its buyer have no cause to say
His money is but lost or thrown away.
Yea, may this second pilgrim yield that fruit,
As may with each good pilgrim's fancy suit;
And may it persuade some that go astray,
To turn their foot and heart to the right way —

Is the hearty prayer of the author, John Bunyan.

Interpreter's house

Christiana and Mercy drew near to a house which was built
for the relief of pilgrims, as you will find more fully related
in the first part of these records of the Pilgrim's Progress.
So they drew on towards the house (the house of the
Interpreter), and when they came to the door they heard a
great talk in the house. They then gave ear, and heard, as
they thought, Christiana mentioned by name; for you must
know that there went before her a talk of her and her children's going on pilgrimage; and this thing was the more
pleasing to them, because they had heard that she was
Christian's wife — that woman who was some time ago so
unwilling to hear of going on pilgrimage. Thus, therefore,
they stood still, and heard the good people within com-
mending her who, they little thought, stood at the door. At
last Christiana knocked. Now when she had knocked, there
came to the door a young girl named Innocent, and opened

the door, and looked. Two women were there. Then the girl said to them, 'Who do you want to speak to here?'

Christiana answered, 'We understand that this is a privileged place for those who have become pilgrims, and we who are at this door now are pilgrims. So please may we have what we came for – the day is very far spent, as you see, and we are loth tonight to go any farther.'

The girl answered, 'What may I call you, that I may tell your name to my Lord within?'

'My name is Christiana,' was the reply. 'I was the wife of the pilgrim who some years ago travelled this way, and these are his four children. Also, this girl is my companion, and is going on pilgrimage too.'

Then Innocent ran in and said to those within, 'Can you think who is at the door? There is Christiana and her children, and her companion, all waiting for hospitality here.'

Then they leaped for joy, and went and told their master. So he came to the door, and looking upon her, he said, 'Are you that Christiana whom Christian, the good man, left behind him when he betook himself to a pilgrim's life?'

'I am that woman,' admitted Christiana, 'that was so hard-hearted as to slight my husband's troubles, and left him to go on his journey alone, and these are his four children; but now I have come too, and I am convinced that no way is right but this.'

'Then,' said Interpreter, 'this fulfils what is written of the man who said to his son, "Go, work today in my vineyard," and he said to his father, "I will not," but afterwards repented, and went' (Matthew 21:29).

Then Christiana said, 'So be it. Amen. God make it a true saying upon me, and grant that I may be found at the last by him in peace without spot and blameless.'

Then Interpreter said, 'But why are you standing like this at the door? Come in, daughter of Abraham; we were talking of you just now, for tidings have already come to us how you have become a pilgrim. Come, children, come in; come, girl, come in.' So he had them all into his house.

So when they were within, they were invited to sit down and rest; when they had done so, those that attended upon the pilgrims in the house came into the room to see them. And one smiled, and another smiled, and they all smiled for joy that Christiana had become a pilgrim. They also looked at the boys; they stroked them over the faces with the hand, in token of their kind reception of them; and they bade them all welcome into their master's house.

After a while, because supper was not ready, the Interpreter took them into his significant rooms, and showed them what Christian, Christiana's husband, had seen some time before. Here, therefore, they saw the man in the cage, the man and his dream, the man that cut his way through his enemies, and the picture of the biggest of them all, together with the rest of those things that were then so profitable to Christian.

This done, and after these things had been somewhat digested by Christiana and her company, the Interpreter took them into a room where was a man who could look no way but downwards, with a muck-rake in his hand. There was also someone standing over him with a celestial crown in his hand, offering to give him that crown for his muck-rake; but the man did not look up, but raked the straws, the small sticks, and dust of the floor to himself.

Then said Christiana, 'I think I know the meaning of this, for this is a figure of a man of this world, isn't it?'

'You are right,' said Interpreter, 'and his muck-rake shows his carnal mind. You see him concentrating on raking up straws and sticks and the dust of the floor, rather than on what the man says who is calling to him from above with the celestial crown in his hand. This is to show that heaven is like a fable to some, and that things here are counted the only things substantial. Now, you were also shown that the man could look no way but downwards; this is to let thee know that earthly things, when they are with power upon men's minds, quite carry their hearts away from God.'

Then said Christiana, 'Oh, deliver me from this muck-rake!'

'That prayer,' said the Interpreter, 'has lain by till it is almost rusty. "Give me not riches" (Proberbs 30:8) is scarcely the prayer of one in ten thousand. Straws, and sticks, and dust with most are the great things now looked after.'

With that Mercy and Christiana wept, and said, 'It is, alas, too true!'

When the Interpreter had shown them this, he took them into the very best room in the house (a very fine brave room it was); so he invited them to look round about, and see if they could find anything profitable there. Then they looked round and round, for there was nothing to be seen there except a very great spider on the wall, and that they overlooked.

Then said Mercy, 'Sir, I see nothing'. But Christiana held her peace.

But the Interpreter said, 'Look again'. She therefore looked again, and said, 'There is nothing here but an ugly spider, who hangs by her hands upon the wall.' Then he said, 'Is there only one spider in all this spacious room?' Then Christiana's eyes filled with tears, for she was a woman quick of apprehension, and she said, 'Yes, lord, there is here more than one — and spiders whose venom is far more destructive than that which is in her.' The Interpreter then looked pleasantly upon her, and said, 'You have said the truth'. This made Mercy blush, and the boys to cover their faces; for they all began now to understand the riddle.

Then said the Interpreter again, '"The spider taketh hold with her hands," as you see, "and is in kings' palaces" (Proverbs 30:28). And this is recorded in order to show you that however full of the venom of sin you may be, you may, by the hand of faith, lay hold of and dwell in the best room that belongs to the king's house above.'

'I thought,' said Christiana, 'of something of this; but I

could not imagine it all. I thought that we were like spiders, and that we looked like ugly creatures, in whatever fine room we were, but that by this spider, this venomous and ill-favoured creature, we were to learn how to act faith, that did not enter my mind. And yet she has taken hold with her hands, as I see, and dwells in the best room in the house. God has made nothing in vain.'

Then they seemed all to be glad, but the water stood in their eyes. Yet they looked one upon another, and also bowed before the Interpreter.

He led them then into another room where there was a hen and her chicks, and told them to observe for a while. One of the chicks went to the trough to drink, and every time she drank she lifted up her head and her eyes towards heaven. 'See,' he said, 'what this little chick does, and learn from her to acknowledge from where your mercies come, by receiving them by looking up. Yet again,' he said, 'observe and look.' So they watched, and saw that the hen called to her chicks in four ways.

1. She had a common call, and that she made all day long.

2. She had a special call, and that she only used occasionally.

3. She had a brooding note.

4. She had an outcry (Matthew 23:37).

'Now,' said Interpreter, 'compare this hen to your king, and these chicks to his obedient ones. For, in the same way as she does, he himself has his ways of calling his people. By his common call, he gives nothing; by his special call, he always has something to give; he also has a brooding voice for those who are under his wing; and he has an outcry, my darlings, to give the alarm when he sees the enemy coming. I chose, my darlings, to lead you into the room where such things are, because you are women, and they are easy for you.'

'And, sir,' said Christiana, 'let us see some more.'

So he led them into the slaughterhouse, where a butcher

was killing a sheep. And the sheep was quiet, and took her death patiently. Then said the Interpreter, 'You must learn from this sheep to suffer, and to put up with wrongs without murmurings and complaints. Behold how quietly she takes her death; and, without objecting, she allows her skin to be pulled over her ears. Your king calls you his sheep.'

After this, he led them into his garden, where there was a great variety of flowers. And he said, 'Do you see all these?' So Christiana said, 'Yes'. Then he said again, 'See, the flowers vary in height, in quality, and colour, and smell, and virtue, and some are better than others. Also, where the gardener has set them, there they stand, and do not quarrel with one another.'

Again, he took them into his field, which he had sowed with wheat and corn; but when they looked at it, all the tops had been cut off, only the straw remaining. He said again, 'This ground was manured, and ploughed, and sown, but what shall we do with the crop?'

Then said Christiana, 'Burn some, and make muck of the rest.'

Then said the Interpreter again, 'Fruit, you see, is what you look for, and for lack of that you condemn it to the fire, and to be trodden underfoot by people. Beware that in this you do not condemn yourselves.'

Then, as they were coming in from outside, they saw a little robin with a great spider in his mouth. So the Interpreter said, 'Look there'. So they looked, and Mercy wondered. But Christiana said, 'What a disparagement it is to such a pretty little bird as the robin redbreast. He is also a bird above many, that loves to maintain a kind of sociableness with man! I thought they lived upon crumbs of bread, or upon other such harmless matter. I like him worse than I did.'

The Interpreter replied, 'This robin is a very suitable image of some who profess to believe; for to look at they are like this robin, with a pretty song, colour, and bearing;

they seem also to have a very great love for those who make a sincere profession; and above all, to desire to associate with and to be in their company, as if they could live upon the good man's crumbs. They pretend also, that that is why they frequent the house of the godly, and the appointments of the Lord; but when they are by themselves, like the robin, they can catch and gobble up spiders, they can change their diet, drink iniquity, and swallow down sin like water.'

So when they came back into the house, because supper was not yet ready, Christiana again asked the Interpreter to either show or tell them some other things that were profitable.

Then the Interpreter began and said, 'The fatter the sow is, the more she desires the mire; the fatter the ox is, the more willingly he goes to the slaughter; and the more healthy the lusty man is, the more prone he is to evil.

'There is a desire in women to go neat and fine; and it is a comely thing to be adorned with what in God's sight is of great price.

'It is easier to stay awake a night or two, than to sit up a whole year together: so it is easier for someone to begin to profess well, than to hold out as he should to the end.

'Every ship's master, when in a storm, will willingly cast overboard what is of the smallest value to the vessel. But who will throw the best out first? Only someone who does not fear God.

'One leak will sink a ship; and one sin will destroy a sinner.

'Anyone who forgets his friend is ungrateful to him; but anyone who forgets his Saviour is unmerciful to himself.

'Anyone who lives in sin, and looks for happiness hereafter, is like a person who sows cockle, and thinks to fill his barn with wheat or barley.

'If a person wants to live well, let him fetch his last day to him, and make it always his company-keeper.

'Whispering, and change of thoughts, prove that sin is in

the world.

'If the world, which God sets light by, is counted a thing of that worth with men; what is heaven, which God commends?

'If the life that is attended with so many troubles is so loth to be let go by us, what is the life above?

'Everybody will cry up the goodness of men; but who is there that is affected, as he should be, by the goodness of God?

'We seldom sit down to meat but we eat, and leave some; so there is in Jesus Christ more merit and righteousness than the whole world has need of.'

When the Interpreter had done, he took them out into his garden again, to a tree whose inside was all rotten and gone, and yet it grew and had leaves. Then Mercy said, 'What is the meaning of this?'

'This tree,' he said, 'whose outside is fair, and whose inside is rotten, is what many may be compared to who are in God's garden. With their mouths, they speak high about God, but indeed will do nothing for him; whose leaves are fair, but their heart is good for nothing but to be tinder for the devil's tinder-box.'

Now supper was ready, the table spread, and all things set on the board. So they sat down and ate, when thanks had been given. And the Interpreter usually entertained those who lodged with him with music at meals, so the minstrels played. There was also a singer; and a very fine voice he had.

His song was this:

> The Lord is only my support,
> And he that doth me feed:
> How can I then want anything
> Whereof I stand in need?

When the song and music were ended, the Interpreter asked Christiana what it was that at first did move her to adopt a pilgrim's life.

Christiana answered, 'First, the loss of my husband came into my mind, which made me heartily grieved. But all that was only natural affection. Then, after that, the troubles of my husband's pilgrimage came into my mind, and also how churlishly I had behaved to him about it. So guilt took hold of my mind, and would have drawn me into the pond, but that fortunately I had a dream of the well-being of my husband, and a letter sent me by the king of that country where my husband dwells, to come to him. The dream and the letter together so worked on my mind, that they forced me to this way.'

'But,' asked the Interpreter, 'did you meet with no opposition before you set out?'

'Yes, a neighbour of mine, Mrs Timorous (she was related to the man who wanted to persuade my husband to go back for fear of the lions). She almost fooled me, and referred to my pilgrimage as my intended desperate adventure. She also urged what she could to dishearten me – the hardship and troubles that my husband met with on the way; but all this I got over pretty well. But a dream that I had, of two ill-looking people that I thought were plotting how to make me miscarry in my journey, that troubled me much; indeed, it still runs in my mind, and makes me afraid of everyone that I meet, lest they should meet me to do me a mischief, and to turn me out of the way. Indeed, I may tell you, though I would not have everybody know it, that between this and the gate by which we got into the way, we were both so sorely assaulted that we were made to cry out murder; and the two that made this assault upon us were like the two that I saw in my dream.'

Then the Interpreter said, 'Your beginning is good; your end will greatly increase.' So he addressed himself to Mercy, and said to her, 'And what moved you to come here, my dear?'

Then Mercy blushed and trembled, and for a while remained silent.

Then he said, 'Do not be afraid; only believe, and speak

your mind.'

So she began, and said, 'Truly, sir, my lack of experience is what makes me long to be silent, and also fills me with fears of coming short at last. I cannot tell of visions and dreams as my friend Christiana can; nor do I know what it is to mourn for my refusing the counsel of those that were good relations.'

The Interpreter asked, 'What was it, then, dear heart, that has prevailed with you to do as you have done?'

'Why,' replied Mercy, 'when our friend here was packing up to be gone from our town, I and another happened to go to see her; so we knocked at the door, and went in. When we were within, and seeing what she was doing, we asked what she meant to do. She said she was sent for to go to her husband; and then she up and told us how she had seen him in a dream, living in a curious place among immortals, wearing a crown, playing a harp, eating and drinking at his prince's table, and singing praises to him for bringing him there. Now I thought to myself, while she was telling these things to us, my heart burned within me, and I said in my heart, if this is true, I will leave my father and my mother, and the land where I was born, and will, if I may, go along with Christiana.

'So I asked her further of the truth of these things, and if she would let me go with her; for I saw now that to live any longer in our town could only be with the danger of ruin. But yet I came away with a heavy heart; not that I was unwilling to come away, but so many of my relations were left behind. And I have come with all the desire of my heart, and will go, if I may, with Christiana to her husband and his king.'

Then the Interpreter said to her: 'Your setting out is good, for you have given credit to the truth. You are a Ruth, who, for the love that she bore to Naomi and to the Lord her God, left father and mother, and her native land, to come out, and go with a people that she did not know before. "May the Lord repay you for what you have done.

May you be richly rewarded by the Lord, the God of Israel, under whose wings you have come to take refuge"' (Ruth 2:11–12).

Now supper was ended, and preparations were made for bed; the women were put singly alone, and the boys by themselves. Now when Mercy was in bed, she could not sleep for joy that now her doubts of eventual failure were removed farther from her than ever they were before; so she lay blessing and praising God, who had had such favour for her.

In the morning they arose with the sun, and prepared themselves for their departure, but the Interpreter wanted them to wait a while. 'For,' he said, 'you must go from here properly.' Then he said to the girl who had originally opened the door to them, 'Take them into the garden to the bath, and there wash them, and make them clean from the soil which they have gathered by travelling.' Then Innocent took them, and led them into the garden, and brought them to the bath. Then she told them that there they must wash and be clean, for that was the wish of her master for the women who called at his house as they were going on pilgrimage. They then went in and washed, they and the boys and all, and they came out of that bath not only sweet and clean, but also much enlivened and strengthened in their joints; so when they came in, they looked a good deal better than when they went out to wash.

When they returned from the bath in the garden the Interpreter took them and looked at them, and said to them, 'Fair as the moon'. Then he called for the seal with which people who were washed in his bath used to be sealed. So the seal was brought, and he set his mark upon them, that they might be known in the places where they were yet to go. Now the seal was the contents and sum of the Passover which the children of Israel ate when they came out of the land of Egypt (Exodus 13:8–10), and the mark was set between their eyes. This seal greatly added to their beauty, for it was an ornament to their faces; it also added to their gravity, and made them look more like angels.

Then the Interpreter said again to the girl who waited on these women, 'Go into the vestry, and fetch out garments for these people.' So she went, and fetched out white clothes, and laid them down before him, so he commanded them to put them on. 'It was fine linen, white and clean.' When the women were adorned like this, they seemed frightened of each other, for each of them could see the glory on the other but not on herself. Now, therefore, they began to esteem each other better than themselves, 'For you are more beautiful than I am,' said one; 'And you are more comely than I am,' said another. The children also stood amazed to see what they now looked like.

The Interpreter then called for a man-servant of his, Greatheart, and asked him to take sword, and helmet, and shield, 'And take these my daughters,' he said, 'and conduct them to the house called Beautiful, at which place they will rest next.' So he took his weapons, and went before them; and the Interpreter said, 'God speed'. Those who belonged to the family also sent them away with many a good wish; so they went on their way, and sang:

> This place has been our second stage;
> Here we have heard and seen
> Those good things that, from age to age,
> To others hid have been.
> The Dunghill-raker, Spider, Hen,
> The Chicken too, to me
> Hath taught a lesson, let me then
> Conformed to it be.
> The Butcher, Garden, and the Field,
> The Robin and his bait,
> Also the Rotten Tree, doth yield
> Me argument of weight,
> To move me for to watch and pray,

To strive to be sincere,
To take my cross up day by day,
And serve the Lord with fear.

Greatheart

Now I saw in my dream that they went on, and Greatheart
went before them, so they went and came to a place where
Christian's burden fell off his back and tumbled into a
sepulchre. Here, then, they paused, and here also they
blessed God. 'Now,' said Christiana, 'it comes to my mind
what was said to us at the gate – that we should have pardon by word and deed: by word, that is, by the promise; by
deed, that is, in the way it was obtained. What the promise
is, of that I know something; but what is it to have pardon
by deed, or in the way that it was obtained? Mr Greatheart,
I suppose you know; so, if you please, let us hear you tell
us about it.'

Greatheart said: 'Pardon by the deed done is pardon
obtained by someone for another who had need of it.'

'Not by the person pardoned,' says someone else, 'but in
the way in which I have obtained it.'

'So, then, to speak to the question in more detail, the
pardon that you and Mercy and these boys have attained
was obtained by another, that is, by the one who let you in
at the gate; and he has obtained it in this double way – he
has performed righteousness to cover you, and spilt blood
to wash you in.'

Christiana said: 'But if he parts with his righteousness to
us, what will he have for himself?'

Greatheart replied: 'He has more righteousness than
you need, or than he needs himself.'

'Please explain that,' said Christiana.

'With all my heart,' said Greaheart. 'But first I must
explain that the person we are now about to speak of is
someone without equal. He has two natures in one person

– plain to be distinguished, impossible to be divided. Each of these natures has a righteousness, and each righteousness is essential to that nature. So one may as easily cause the nature to be extinct, as to separate its justice or righteousness from it. Of these righteousnesses, therefore, we are not made partakers so as that they, or either of them, should be put upon us that we might be made just, and live thereby. Besides these there is a righteousness which this person has, as these two natures are joined in one. And this is not the righteousness of the Godhead as distinguished from the manhood, nor the righteousness of the manhood as distinguished from the Godhead; but a righteousness which belongs to the union of both natures, and may properly be called the righteousness that is essential to his being prepared by God for the mediatory office which he was to be entrusted with. If he parts with his first righteousness, he parts with his Godhead; if he parts with his second righteousness, he parts with the purity of his manhood; if he parts with this third, he parts with that perfection that enables him to mediate. He has, therefore, another righteousness which stands in performance, or obedience to a revealed will. This is what he puts on sinners, through which their sins are covered. Thus, "As by one man's disobedience many were made sinners, so by the obedience of one shall many be made righteous"' (Romans 5:19).

'But are the other righteousnesses of no use to us?' asked Christiana.

'Yes, for though they are essential to his natures and office, and so cannot be communicated to anyone else, it is still by virtue of them that the righteousness that justifies is, for that purpose, efficacious. The righteousness of his Godhead gives virtue to his obedience; the righteousness of his manhood gives capability to his obedience to justify; and the righteousness that stands in the union of these two natures to his office, gives authority to that righteousness to do the work for which it is ordained.

'So, then, here is a righteousness that Christ, as God, has no need of, for he is God without it; here is a righteousness that Christ, as man, has no need of to make him so, for he is perfect man without it; again, here is a righteousness that Christ, as God-man, has no need of, for he is perfectly so without it. Here, then, is a righteousness that Christ, as God, as man, and God-man, has no need of with reference to himself, and therefore he can spare it — a justifying righteousness, that he, for himself, lacks nothing, and therefore he gives it away. Hence it is called "the gift of righteousness" (Romans 5:17). This righteousness, since Christ Jesus the Lord has made himself under the law, must be given away; for the law not only binds those under it to act justly, but to be charitable; so they *must,* they *ought* by the law, if they have two coats, to give one to him who has none. Now our Lord indeed has two coats, one for himself and one to spare, and so he freely gives one to those who have none. And thus, Christiana and Mercy and the rest of you that are here, your pardon comes by deed, or by the work of another man. Your Lord Christ is he who has worked, and has given away what he did to the next poor beggar he meets.

'But again, in order to pardon by deed, something must be paid to God as a price, as well as something prepared to cover us. Sin has delivered us up to the just curse of a righteous law. Now from this curse we must be justified by way of redemption, a price being paid for the harm we have done, and this is by the blood of your Lord, who came and stood in your place and stead, and died your death for your transgressions (Romans 4:24). Thus he has ransomed you from your transgressions by blood, and covered your polluted and deformed souls with righteousness. Therefore God passes over you, and will not hurt you when he comes to judge the world (Galatians 3:13).'

'Now I see that there was something to be learnt by our being pardoned by word and deed,' said Christiana. 'Let us try to keep this in mind, Mercy; and, my children, you must remember it too. But, sir, wasn't it this that made my good Christian's burden fall from off his shoulder, and that made him give three leaps for joy?'

'Yes,' said Greatheart, 'it was believing this that cut those strings that could not be cut by other means; and it was to give him a proof of the virtue of that that he was allowed to carry his burden to the cross.'

'I thought so,' continued Christiana, 'for though my heart was light and joyful before, yet it is ten times lighter and more joyful now. And I am persuaded by what I have felt, though I have felt but little as yet, that if the most burdened man in the world was here, and saw and believed as I now do, it would make his heart the more merry and blithe.'

Greatheart went on: 'Seeing and considering these not only brings us comfort and ease from a burden, but an endeared affection is born in us through it. For if just once you think that pardon comes, not only by promise, but thus, you must be affected with the way and means of your redemption, and so with the man who has wrought it for you.'

'True,' said Christiana. 'I think it makes my heart bleed to think that he should bleed for me. O loving one! O blessed one! You deserve to have me; you have bought me. You deserve to have me all; you have paid for me ten thousand times more than I am worth. No wonder this made the tears come to my husband's eyes, and made him trudge so nimbly on. I am persuaded he wished me with him; but, vile wretch that I was, I let him come all alone. O Mercy, I wish that your father and mother were here, yes, and Mrs Timorous also. I wish now with all my heart that here was Madam Wanton too. Surely, surely their hearts would be affected, nor could the fear of one, nor the powerful desires of the other, prevail with them to go home again, and to refuse to become good pilgrims.'

'You speak now in the warmth of your affections,' said Greatheart. 'Will it, do you think, be always thus with you?

Besides, this is not communicated to everyone, nor to everyone who sees your Jesus bleed. There were some among those who stood by, and who saw the blood run from his heart to the ground, who did not lament, but rather laughed at him. Instead of becoming his disciples they hardened their hearts against him. All that you have, my daughters, you have through a special impression made by a divine contemplating upon what I have told you. Remember what you were told, that the hen, by her common call, gave no food to her chicks. Therefore, what you have comes through special grace.'

Simple, Sloth and Presumption

Now I saw, still in my dream, that they went on until they came to the place where Simple and Sloth and Presumption lay down and slept when Christian went by on pilgrimage. They were hung up in irons a little way off on the other side.

Then Mercy said to their guide, 'What are those three men? And what are they hanging there for?'

Greatheart answered, 'These three men were men of very bad qualities. They had no desire to be pilgrims themselves, and whoever they could they hindered. They were for sloth and folly themselves, and whoever they could persuade, they made so too; and taught them to presume that they would be all right in the end. They were asleep when Christian went by, and now as you go by, they are hanged.'

'But,' asked Mercy, 'could they persuade anyone to be of their opinion?'

'Yes,' replied Greaheart. 'They turned several from the way. There was Slowpace that they persuaded to do as they did. They also prevailed with someone called Shortwind, and someone called No-heart, and with another called Linger-after-desire, and with Sleepyhead, and with a young woman – her name was Dull – to turn out of the way and become like them. Besides, they brought up an ill report of your Lord, persuading others that he was a taskmaster. They also brought up an evil report of the good land, saying it was not half so good as some claim. They also began to vilify his servants, and to count the very best of them meddlesome, troublesome busy-bodies: further, they would call the bread of God, husks; the comforts of his children, fancies; the labour of pilgrims, things to no purpose.'

'Well,' said Christiana, 'if they were like that, they will never be mourned by me; they only got what they deserved, and I think it is good that they hang so near the highway, that others may see and take warning. But would it not have been good if their crimes had been engraved on some plate of iron or brass, and left here, where they did their mischiefs, for a warning to other bad men?'

'So it is,' said Greaheart, 'as you can see if you will go a little to the wall.'

'No, no,' said Mercy, 'let them hang, and their names rot, and their crimes live for ever against them. I think it a high favour that they were hanged before we came here. Otherwise, who knows what else they may have done to such women as us?'

Then she turned it into a song, saying:

> Now then, you three, hang there and be a sign
> To all that shall against the truth combine:
> And let him that comes after fear this end,
> If unto pilgrims he is not a friend.
> And thou, my soul, of all such men beware,
> That unto holiness opposers are.

The Hill Difficulty

Thus they went on till they came to the foot of the Hill Difficulty, where again their good friend Mr Greatheart took the opporunity to tell them about what happened there when Christian himself went by. So he led them first to the spring.

'There!' he said. 'This is the spring that Christian drank from before he went up this hill, and then it was clear and good; but now it is dirty with the feet of some who do not desire pilgrims to quench their thirst here' (Ezekiel 34:18).

Mercy then said, 'And why are they so envious, do you think?'

Greatheart, their guide, replied, 'It will be all right if it is taken up and put into a vessel that is sweet and good; for then the dirt will sink to the bottom, and the water comes out by itself more clear.' So Christiana and her companion were compelled to do that. They took it up, and put it into an earthenware pot, and so let it stand till the dirt had gone to the bottom, and then they drank from it.

Next he showed them the two by-ways that were at the foot of the hill, where Formality and Hypocrisy lost themselves. And he said, 'These are dangerous paths. Two people were cast away here when Christian came by. And although, as you see, these ways have since been blocked with chains, posts, and a ditch, yet there are people that will choose to adventure here, rather than take the trouble of going up the hill.'

Christiana said, '"The way of transgressions is hard" (Proverbs 13:15). It's a wonder that they can get into those ways without danger of breaking their necks.'

Greatheart said, 'They will try; indeed, if at any time any of the king's servants happens to see them, and calls them, and tells them that they are in the wrong ways, and bids them beware the danger, then they will answer them back, and say, "As for what you have said to us in the name of the king, we willl not listen to you; but we will certainly do whatever we ourselves say" (Jeremiah 44:16–17). If you look a little farther, you will see that these ways are made cautionary enough, not only by these posts, and ditch, and chain, but also by being hedged up; yet they will choose to go there.'

'They are silly,' said Christiana. 'They do not like taking trouble; going up-hill is unpleasant to them. So what is written comes true: "The way of the slothful man is a hedge of thorns" (Proverbs 15:19). They would rather to walk on a snare than go up this hill and the rest of this way to the city.'

Then they set forward, and began to go up the hill, and up the hill they went; but before they got to the top, Christiana began to pant, and said, 'I dare say this is a breathing hill; no wonder those that love their ease more than their souls choose a smoother way.'

Then said Mercy, 'I must sit down'. And the smallest of the children began to cry.

'Come, come,' said Greatheart, 'do not sit down here, for the prince's arbour is just above.' Then he took the little boy by the hand, and led him up to it.

When they came to the arbour, they were very willing to sit down; for they were all in a pelting heat. Then said Mercy, 'How sweet is rest to those who labour! And how good is the prince of pilgrims to provide such resting-places for them! (Matthew 11:28). I have heard a lot about this arbour, but I never saw it before. But let us beware of sleeping here; for I have heard that it cost poor Christian dear.'

Then said Mr Greatheart to the little ones, 'What do you think now of going on pilgrimage?'

'Sir,' said the youngest, 'I was almost beaten out of heart, but I thank you for lending me a hand when I needed it. And I remember now what my mother has told me, namely, that the way to heaven is like going up a ladder, and the way to hell is like going down a hill. But I would rather go up the ladder to life, than down the hill to death.'

Then Mercy said, 'But the proverb is, "To go down the hill is easy."'

But James said (for that was his name), 'The day is coming when, in my opinion, going down hill will be the hardest of all.'

'That's a good boy,' said his master. 'You have given her a right answer.' Then Mercy smiled; but the little boy blushed.

'Come,' said Christiana, 'will you eat a bit, a little to sweeten your mouths while you sit here to rest your legs? For I have here a piece of pomegranate which Mr Interpreter put in my hand just when I came out of his house; he also gave me a piece of honeycomb and a little bottle of spirits.'

'I thought he gave you something,' said Mercy, 'because he called you to one side.'

'Yes, so he did,' said the other, 'but, Mercy, it will still be as I said it would, when we first left home; you will share in all the good that I have, because you became my companion so willingly.' Then she gave some to them, and they did eat, both Mercy and the boys.

And Christiana said to Mr Greatheart, 'Sir, will you do the same as we are doing?'

But he answered, 'You are going on pilgrimage, and presently I shall return; much good may what you have do to you. At home I eat the same every day.' Now when they had eaten and drunk, and had chatted a little longer, their guide said to them, 'The day is wearing away; if you think good, let us prepare to be going.'

So they got up to go, and the little boys went in front; but Christiana forgot to take her bottle of spirits with her, so she sent her little boy back to fetch it. Then Mercy said, 'I think this is a losing place. Here Christian lost his roll, and here Christiana left her bottle behind her. Sir, what is the cause of this?'

So their guide answered, 'The cause is sleep or forgetfulness. Some sleep when they should keep awake, and some forget when they should remember; and this is the very reason why often, at the resting-places, some pilgrims in some things come off losers. In their greatest enjoyments, pilgrims should watch and remember what they have already received; but because they do not do so, often their rejoicing ends in tears, and their sunshine in a cloud: witness the story of Christian in this place.'

Now, they heard that there was a post come from the Celestial City with matter of great importance to Christiana, the wife of Christian the pilgrim. So inquiry was made for her, and the house was found out where she was, so the post presented her with a letter. The contents said, 'Greetings, good woman, I bring you news that the master is calling for you, and waiting for you to stand in his presence, in clothes of immortality, within this next ten days.'

When he had read this letter to her, he gave her a sign that he was a true messenger, and had come to tell her to make haste to be gone. The sign was an arrow with a point, sharpened with love, let easily into her heart, which by degrees worked so effectively with her, that at the time appointed she must be gone.

When Christiana saw that her time had come, and that she was the first of this company that was to go over, she called for Mr Greatheart, her guide, and told him how matters were. So he told her he was heartily glad of the news, and would have been glad had the post come for him. Then she asked him to give her advice how everything should be prepared for her journey.

So he told her, saying it should be done in such and such a manner – 'and we who survive will accompany you to the riverside.'

Then she called for her children, and gave them her blessing; and told them that she was still comforted by reading the mark on their foreheads, and was glad to see them with her there, and that they had kept their garments so white. Lastly, she bequeathed to the poor what little she had, and commanded her sons and her daughters to be ready when the messenger came for them.

When she had spoken these words to her guide and to her children, she called for Mr Valiant-for-truth, and said to him, 'Sir, you have in all places shown yourself true-hearted. Be faithful to death, and my king will give you a crown of life. I would also entreat you to keep an eye on my children; and if at any time you see them faint, speak comfortingly to them. For my daughters, my sons' wives, they have been faithful; and a fulfilling of the promise to them will be their end.' But she gave Mr Standfast a ring.

Then she called for old Mr Honest, and said of him, 'Behold an Israelite indeed, in whom is no guile.' Then he said, 'I wish you a fair day when you set out for Mount Zion, and shall be glad to see that you go over the river dry shod.' But she answered, 'Come wet, come dry, I long to be gone; for however the weather is on my journey, I shall have time enough when I come there to sit down and rest and get dry.'

Then came in that good man Mr Ready-to-halt to see her. So she said to him, 'Your travel here has been with difficulty; but that will make your rest the sweeter. But watch, and be ready; for when you are not expecting it, the messenger may come.'

After him came in Mr Despondency and his daughter Much-afraid, to whom she said, 'You ought always to remember with thankfulness your deliverance from the hands of Giant Despair and out of Doubting Castle. The effect of that mercy is, that you have been brought here in safety. Be watchful, and cast away fear; be sober, and hope to the end.'

Then she said to Mr Feeble-mind, 'You were delivered from the mouth of giant Slay-good, that you might live in the light of the living for ever, and see your king with comfort. Only I advise you to repent of your aptness to fear and doubt of his goodness before he sends for you, lest, when he comes, you are forced to stand before him for that fault with blushing.'

Now the day drew on that Christiana must be gone. So the road was full of people to see her take her journey. But all the banks beyond the river were full of horses and chariots, which had come down from above to accompany her to the city gate. So she came out, and entered the river with a gesture of farewell to those that followed her to the riverside. The last word she was heard to say here was, 'I am coming, Lord, to be with you, and bless you.'

So her children and friends returned to their place, for those that were for Christiana had carried her out of their sight. So she went and called, and entered in at the gate with all the ceremonies of joy that her husband Christian had done before her.

At her departure her children wept, but Mr Greatheart and Mr Valiant played on the well-tuned cymbal and harp for joy. So they all departed to their respective places.

In time a post came to the town again, and his business was with Mr Ready-to-halt. So he inquired him out, and said to him, 'I have come to you in the name of him whom you have loved and followed, though upon crutches. And my message is to tell you that he expects you at his table to eat with him in his kingdom the next day after Easter. So prepare for this journey.'

Then he also gave him a sign that he was a true messenger, saying, 'I have broken your golden bowl, and loosened your silver cord' (Ecclesiastes 12:6).

After this, Mr Ready-to-halt called for his fellow-pilgrims, and told them, saying, 'I am sent for, and God will surely visit you also.' So he asked Mr Valiant to make his will. And because he had nothing to bequeath to those who would survive him but his crutches and his good wishes, he said, 'These crutches I bequeath to my son that shall tread in my steps, with an hundred warm wishes that he may prove better than I have done.'

Then he thanked Mr Greatheart for his conduct and kindness, and so addressed himself to his journey. When he came to the brink of the river, he said, 'Now I shall have no more need of these crutches, since there are chariots and horses over there for me to ride on.' The last words he was heard to say were, 'Welcome, life!' So he went his way.

After this, Mr Feeble-mind had news brought him that the post sounded his horn at his door. Then he came in and told him, saying, 'I have come to tell you that your master needs you, and that in very little time you must see his face in brightness. And take this as a token of the truth of my message. "Those that look out at the windows shall be darkened" (Ecclesiastes 12:3).'

Then Mr Feeble-mind called for his friends, and told them what message had been brought to him, and what token he had received of the truth of the message. Then he said, 'Since I have nothing to bequeath to anyone, why should I make a will? As for my feeble mind, that I will leave behind me, for I have no need of that where I am going; nor is it worth bestowing upon the poorest pilgrim; so, when I am gone, I would like you, Mr Valiant, to bury it in a dunghill.' This done, and the day having come when he was to depart, he entered the river just like the rest. His last words were, 'Hold out, faith and patience'. So he went over to the other side.

When many days had passed, Mr Despondency was sent for. A post came and brought this message to him: 'Trembling man, these are to summon you to be ready with your King, by the next Lord's day, to shout for joy for your deliverance from all your doubts.'

And, said the messenger, 'Take this for a proof that my message is true.' So he gave him the grasshopper to be a burden to him (Ecclesiastes 3:5). Now Mr Despondency's daughter, whose name was Much-afraid, said, when she heard what was done, that she would go with her father. Then Mr Despondency said to his friends, 'Myself and my daughter, you know what we have been, and how troublesomely we have behaved ourselves in every company. My will and my daughter's is, that no one ever receive our desponds and slavish fears from the day of our departure for ever; for I know that after my death, they will offer themselves to others. For, to be plain with you, they are ghosts, which we entertained when we first began to be pilgrims, and could never shake them off afterwards. And they will walk about, and seek to be received by the pilgrims; but for our sakes, shut the doors on them.'

When the time came for them to depart, they went to

the brink of the river. The last words of Mr Despondency
were, 'Farewell night, welcome day!' His daughter went
through the river singing; but none could understand
what she said.

Then, after a while, there was a post in the town that
inquired for Mr Honest. So he came to his house where he
was, and delivered to his hand these lines: 'You are commanded to be ready a week today to present yourself
before your Lord at his Father's house. And as a token that
my message is true, "all the daughters of music shall be
brought low" (Ecclesiastes 12:4).' Then Mr Honest called
for his friends, and said to them, 'I am dying, but shall
make no will. As for my honesty, it shall go with me; let
him that comes after be told of this.' When the day that he
was to be gone arrived, he prepared to go over the river.
Now the river at that time overflowed the banks in some
places. But Mr Honest, in his lifetime, had spoken to someone called Good-conscience to meet him there, which he
did, and lent him his hand, and so helped him over. The
last words of Mr Honest were, 'Grace reigns'. So he left the
world.

After this it was heard that Mr Valiant-for-truth was
taken with a summons by the same post as the other; and
had this for a token that the summons was true, that his
pitcher was broken at the fountain (Ecclesiates 12:6).
When he understood it, he called for his friends, and told
them of it. Then he said, 'I am going to my Father's; and
though I got here with great difficulty, I do not now regret
all the trouble I took to reach where I am. My sword I give
to whoever follows me in my pilgrimage, and my courage
and skill to whoever can get it. My marks and scars I carry
with me, to be a witness for me that I have fought the
battles of the one who will now be my rewarder.' When the
day came for him to go, many accompanied him to the
riverside; and as he went in he said, 'Death, where is your
sting?' And as he went down deeper, he said, 'Grave,
where is your victory?' So he passed over, and all the

trumpets sounded for him on the other side.

Then there came a summons for Mr Standfast (this Mr Standfast was he that the rest of the pilgrims found upon his knees in the Enchanted Ground); for the post brought it him open in his hands. The contents of it were that he must prepare for a change of life, for his master was not willing that he should be so far from him any longer. Mr Standfast wondered about this. 'You need not doubt the truth of my message,' said the messenger, 'for here is a token of its truth: "your well is broken at the cistern" (Ecclesiastes 12:6).' Then he called Mr Greatheart, who was their guide, and said to him, 'Sir, although I did not happen to be in your company much when I was a pilgrim, you have still been helpful to me, since the time I knew you. When I came from home, I left behind me a wife and five small children. Let me entreat you at your return (for I know that you will go, and return to your master's house, in hope that you may lead more of the holy pilgrims), that you send to my family, and let them be acquainted with all that has happened and will happen to me. Tell them, moreover, of my happy arrival at this place, and of the present blessed condition that I am in. Tell them also of Christian and Christiana his wife, and how she and her children came after her husband. Tell them also what a happy end she made, and where she has gone. I have little or nothing to send to my family, except it be prayers and tears for them; it will suffice if you acquaint them of this, in case they may prevail.' When Mr Standfast had thus set things in order, and the time having come for him to hasten away, he also went down to the river. Now there was a great calm at that time in the river, so Mr Standfast, when he was about half-way in, stood awhile, and talked to his companions that had helped him thus far. And he said:

'This river has been a terror to many; yes, the thoughts of it also have often frightened me. But now I stand easy; my foot is fixed where the feet of the priests that bore the ark of the covenant stood, while Israel went over this Jordan (Joshua 3:17). The waters, indeed, are bitter to the palate, and cold to the stomach; yet the thought of what I am going to, and of the help that waits for me on the other side, lie as a glowing coal at my heart.

'I see myself now at the end of my journey, my hard days are over. I am going now to see the head that was crowned with thorns, and the face that was spat upon for me.

'I have formerly lived by hearsay and faith; but now I go where I shall live by sight, and shall be with him in whose company I delight myself.

'I have loved to hear my Lord spoken of, and wherever I have seen the print of his shoe in the earth, there I have longed to set my foot too. His name has been sweeter to me than all perfumes. His voice has been most sweet to me, and his countenance I have more desired than they that have most desired the light of the sun. His word I used to gather for my food, and for antidotes against my faintings. He has held me, and I have kept from mine iniquities; he has strengthened my steps in his way.'

Now while he was talking like this his expression changed, his strong man bowed under him; and after he had said, 'Take me, for I have come to you,' he ceased to be seen by them.

But it was glorious to see how the open region was filled with horses and chariots, with trumpeters and pipers, with singers and players on stringed instruments, to welcome the pilgrims as they went up, and followed one another in at the beautiful gate of the city.

As for Christian's children, the four boys that Christiana brought with her, with their wives and children, I did not stay where I was till they had gone over. Also, since I came away, I heard someone say that they were still alive, and so would be for the increase of the church in that place where they were for a time.

If it is my lot to go that way again, I may give those that desire it an account of what I here am silent about; meantime I bid my reader adieu.

5

The Holy War

Address to the Reader

'Tis strange to me, that they that love to tell
Things done of old, yea, and that do excel
Their equals in Historiology,
Speak not of Mansoul's wars, but let them lie
Dead like old fables, or such worthless things,
That to the reader no advantage brings;
When men, like them, make what they will their own,
Till they know this, are to themselves unknown.
   Of stories I well know there's diverse sorts,
Some foreign, some domestic; and reports
Are thereof made, as fancy leads the writers:
(By books a man may guess at the inditers.)
   Some will again of that which never was,
Nor will be, feign (and that without a cause)
Such matter, raise such mountains, tell such things
Of men, of laws, of countries and of kings;
And in their story seem to be so sage,
And with such gravity clothe every page,
That though their frontispiece says all in vain,
Yet to their way disciples they obtain.
   But, readers, I have somewhat else to do,

Than with vain stories thus to trouble you.
What here I say some men do know so well,
They can with tears of joy the story tell.
    The town of Mansoul is well known to many,
Nor are her troubles doubted of by any
That are acquainted with those histories,
That Mansoul and her wars anatomise.
    Then lend ear to what I do relate
Touching the town of Mansoul, and her state;
How she was lost, took captive, made a slave;
And how against him set, that should her save.
Yea, how by hostile ways she did oppose
Her Lord, and with his enemy did close;
For they are true, he that will them deny,
Must needs the best of records vilify.
For my part, I myself was in the town,
Both when 'twas set up, and when pulling down.
I saw Diabolus in its possession,
And Mansoul also under his oppression.
Yea, I was there when she own'd him for lord,
And to him did submit with one accord.
    When Mansoul trampled upon things divine,
And wallowed in filth as doth a swine:
When she betook herself unto her arms,
Fought her Emmanuel and despised his charms,
Then I was there, and sorely griev'd to see
Diabolus and Mansoul so agree.
    Let no man, then, count me a fable-maker,
Nor make my name or credit a partaker
Of their derision; what is here in view,
Of mine own knowledge I dare say is true.
    I saw the Prince's armed men come down
By troops, by thousands to besiege the town;
I saw the captains, heard the trumpets sound,
And how his forces cover'd all the ground:
Yea, how they set themselves in battle 'ray,
I shall remember to my dying day.

I saw the colours waving in the wind,
And they within to mischief how combin'd
To ruin Mansoul, and to take away
Her Primum Mobile without delay.
I saw the mounts cast up against the town,
And how the slings were plac'd to beat it down;
I heard the stones fly whizzing by my ears;
(What's longer kept in mind, than got in fears?)
I heard them fall, and saw what work they made,
And how old Mors did cover with his shade
The face of Mansoul, and I heard her cry,
Woe worth the day, 'in dying I shall die!'
    I saw the battering rams, and how they play'd
To beat up Ear-gate: and I was afraid,
Not only Ear-gate, but the very town
Would by these battering rams be beaten down.
    I saw the fights, and heard the captains shout,
And in each battle saw who fac'd about:
I saw who wounded were, and who were slain,
And who, when dead, would come to life again.
    I heard the cries of those that wounded were,
(While others fought like men bereft of fear;)
And while they cry, Kill, kill was in mine ears,
The gutters ran not so with blood as tears.
    Indeed the captains did not always fight,
But when they would molest us day and night;
They cry, Up, fall on, let us take the town,
Keep us from sleeping, or from lying down.
I was there when the gates were broken ope,
And saw how Mansoul then was stript of hope.
I saw the captains march into the town,
How there they fought, and did their foes cut down.
    I heard the Prince bid Boanerges go
Up to the castle, and there seize his foe;
And saw him and his fellows bring him down
In chains of great contempt quite through the town.
    I saw Emmanuel, how he possest

His town of Mansoul: and how greatly blest
The town, his gallant town of Mansoul was,
When she received his pardon, lov'd his laws.
   When the Diabolonians were caught,
When tried, and when to execution brought,
Then I was there: yea, I was standing by
When Mansoul did the rebels crucify.
   I also saw Mansoul clad all in white,
And heard her Prince call her his heart's delight;
I saw him put upon her chains of gold,
And rings and bracelets, goodly to behold.
   What shall I say? I heard the people's cries,
And saw the Prince wipe tears from Mansoul's eyes.
I heard the groans, and saw the joy of many.
Tell you of all, I neither will, nor can I;
But by what here I say, you well may see
That Mansoul's matchless wars no fables be.
   Mansoul! the desire of both princes was,
One keep his gain would, t'other gain his loss;
Diabolus would cry, The town is mine;
Emmanuel would plead a right divine
Unto his Mansoul; then to blows they go,
And Mansoul cries, 'These wars will me undo!'
Mansoul, her wars seemed endless in her eyes,
She's lost by one, become another's prize:
And he again that lost her last would swear,
Have her I will, or her in pieces tear.
   Mansoul thus was the very seat of war
Wherefore her troubles greater were by far
Than only where the noise of war is heard,
Or where the shaking of a sword is fear'd!
Or only where the small skirmishes are fought,
Or where the fancy fighteth with a thought.
   She saw the swords of fighting men made red,
And heard the cries of those with them wounded.
Must not her frights, then, be much more by far
Than they that to such doings strangers are?

Or theirs that hear the beating of a drum,
But need not fly for fear from house and home?
   Mansoul not only heard the trumpet sound,
But saw her gallants gasping on the ground;
Wherefore we must not think that she could rest
With them whose greatest earnest is but jest;
Or where the blust'ring threat'nings of great wars
Do end in parlies, or in wording jars.
   Mansoul her mighty wars they do portend
Her weal, her woe, and that world without end;
Wherefore she must be more concern'd than they
Whose fears begin and end the self-same day;
Or where none other harm doth come to him
That is engaged but loss of life and limb;
As all must needs that now do dwell
In Universe, and can this story tell.
   Count me not, then, with them who to amaze
The people, set them on the stars to gaze;
Insinuating with much confidence
They are the only men that have the science
Of some brave creatures; yea, a world they will
Have in each star, though it be past their skill
To make it manifest unto a man
That reason hath, or tell his fingers can.
   But I have too long held thee in the porch,
And kept thee from the sunshine with a torch.
Well, now go forward, step within the door,
And there behold five hundred times much more
Of all sorts of such inward rarities,
As please the mind will, and will feed the eyes,
With those which of a christian, thou wilt see;
Nor do thou go to work without my key,
(In mysteries men do often lose their way)
And also turn it right; if thou would'st know
My riddle, and with my heifer plow;
It lies there in the window. Fare thee well,
My next may be to ring thy passing bell.

In my travels, as I walked through many regions and countries, it was my chance to arrive at that famous continent of
Universe. A very large and spacious country it is: it lies
between the two poles, and just amidst the four points of
heaven. It is a place well watered, and richly adorned with
hills and valleys, bravely situated; and for the most part, at
least where I was, very fruitful; also well people, and a very
sweet air.

The people are not all of one complexion, nor yet of one
language, mode, or way of religion; but differ so much, it
is said, as do the planets themselves: some are right and
some are wrong, just as it happens to be in lesser regions.

In this country, as I said, it was my lot to travel; there
travel I did, and that so long till I had learned much of
their mother tongue, together with the customs and manners of those among whom I was. And, to speak the truth,
I was much delighted to see and hear many things which I
saw and heard among them: indeed, I would, to be sure,
even have lived and died a native among them, I was so
taken with them and their doings, had not my Master sent
for me home to his house, there to do business for him,
and to see business done.

Now there is in the country of Universe a fair and delicate town called Mansoul – a town so interesting for its
buildings, so convenient for its situation, so advantageous
for its privileges (I mean with reference to its origins) that
I may say of it, as was said before of the continent in which
it is placed, 'There is not its equal under the whole heaven'.

As to the situation of this town, it lies between two
worlds: and the first founder and builder of it so far as I
can gather from the best and most authentic records, was
one Shaddai ('Shaddai' means the All-sufficient, or
Almighty); and he built it for his own delight (see Genesis
1:26). He made it the mirror and glory of all that he made,
beyond anything else that he did in that country. Indeed,
so goodly a town was Mansoul, when first built, that some
people say the gods, when it was set up, came down to see

it, and sang for joy. And as he made it good to see, so also
he made it mighty to have dominion over all the country
round about. Everyone was commanded to acknowledge
Mansoul as their capital, all were enjoined to do homage to
it. The town itself had positive commission, and power
from her King to demand service from all, and also to subdue those that denied it in any way.

There was reared up in the midst of this town a most
famous and stately place (the heart of man in his original
state). For strength, it was called a castle; for pleasantness,
a paradise; for largeness, a place so copious as to contain
all the world (see Ecclesiastes 3:11). This place King Shaddai intended for himself alone, and not another with him;
partly because of his own delights, and partly because he
did not want the terror of strangers to be upon the town.
This place Shaddai made also a garrison; but he committed the keeping of it only to the men of the town.

The walls of the town were well built: indeed, so firm
were they knit and compacted together that had it not
been for the townsmen themselves they could not have
been shaken or broken for ever.

For here lay the excellent wisdom of him that built Mansoul, that the walls could never be broken down or hurt by
the most mighty potentates, unless the townsmen gave
consent to it.

This famous town of Mansoul had five gates, at which to
come out, and at which to go in; and these were made like
the walls, that is, impregnable, and such as could never be
opened nor forced without the will and permission of
those within. The names of the gates are these: Ear-gate,
Eye-gate, Mouth-gate, Nose-gate, and Feel-gate.

Other things there were that belonged to the town of
Mansoul, which if you adjoin to these, will give still further
demonstration to all of the glory and strength of the place.
It always had a sufficiency of provision within its walls; it
had the best, most wholesome, and excellent law that was
then extant in the world. There was not a rogue, rascal, or

traitorous person then within its walls: they were all true men, and fast joined together: and this, you know, is a great matter. And to all these it had always, so long as it had the goodness to keep true to Shaddai the king, his protection, and it was his delight.

Well, at this time Diabolus, a mighty giant, made an assault upon this famous town of Mansoul, to take it and make it his own habitation. This giant was at first one of the servants of King Shaddai, by whom he was made, and raised to a most high and mighty place; indeed, he was put into such principalities as belonged to the best of his territories and dominions. This Diabolus was made Son of the Morning (see Isaiah 14:12), and a brave place he had of it. It brought him much glory and gave him much brightness – in income that might have contented his Luciferian heart, had it not been insatiable and enlarged as hell itself.

Seeing himself thus exalted to greatness and honour, and raging in his mind for higher state and degree, he begins to think how he might be set up as lord over all, and have the sole power over Shaddai. (Now the King reserved that for his Son, and had already bestowed it upon him.) So first of all he considers what had best be done, and then tells some others of his companions what he thinks – which they also agreed to. So, in short, they reached this conclusion, that they should make an attempt upon the King's Son to destroy him that the inheritance might be theirs. Well, to be short, the treason, as I said, was concluded, the time appointed, the word given, and the assault attempted. Now the King and his Son being all and always eye, could not but discern all that passed in his dominions, and he having always a love for his Son, as for himself, could not, at what he saw, but be greatly provoked and offended, so what does he do but take them in the very first trip that they made toward their design, convicts them of their treason, and casts them altogether out of all place of trust, benefit, honour and preferment. This done, he banishes them from the court, turns them down into horrid pits, never more to expect the least favour from his hands, but to abide the judgment that he had appointed, and that for ever and ever (see Jude 6).

Now they, being thus cast out of all place of trust, profit and honour, and also knowing that they had lost their Prince's favour, for ever being banished from his court, and cast down to the horrible pits, you may be sure they would now add to their former pride what malice and rage against Shaddai, and against his Son, they could. So, roving and ranging in much fury from place to place (see 1 Peter 5:8), in case they might find something that was the king's to revenge themselves on him by spoiling it, at last they happened on this spacious country of Universe and steered their course toward the town of Mansoul. And considering that that town was one of the chief works and delights of the King Shaddai, what do they do but, after taking counsel, make an assault upon the town. I say they knew that Mansoul belonged to Shaddai, for they were there when he built and beautified it for himself. So when they had found the place, they shouted horribly for joy, and roared on it like a lion on its prey, saying, 'Now, we have found the prize, and how to be revenged on King Shaddai for what he has done to us.' So they sat down and called a council of war; and considered what ways and methods they had best engage in to win for themselves this famous town of Mansoul.

They marched towards Mansoul, but all in a manner invisible, except for one; nor did he approach the town in his own likeness, but under the shape and in the body of the dragon.

So they drew up and sat down before Ear-gate, for that was the place of hearing for everybody outside the town, as Eye-gate was the place of perception. So he came up with his train to the gate, and laid his ambush for Captain Resistance, within bowshot of the town. This done, the giant ascended close up to the gate, and called to the town of Mansoul for audience. Nor did he take anyone with him but someone called Ill-pause, who was his orator in all difficult matters. Now, as I said, he came up to the gate and (as the manner of those times was) sounded his trumpet for audience; at which the chief men of the town of Mansoul, such as Lord Innocent, Lord Will-be-will, the Lord Mayor, Mr Recorder and Captain Resistance, came down to the wall to see who was there, and what was the matter. And Lord Will-be-will, when he looked over and saw who stood at the gate, demanded what he was, and why he had come, and why he roused the town of Mansoul with so unusual a sound.

Diabolus then, as if he had been a lamb, began his oration, and said, 'Gentlemen of the famous town of Mansoul, I live, as you may perceive, not far from you, but near, and am bound by the King to do you my homage, and what service I can: wherefore that I may be faithful to myself and to you, I have something of concern to impart to you; so give me your audience, and hear me patiently. And, first, I will assure you, it is not myself but you, not mine but your advantage, that I seek by what I now do, as will full well be made manifest by my opening my mind to you. For, Gentlemen, I have (to tell you the truth) come to show you how you may obtain great and ample deliverance from a bondage that unawares to yourselves you are enslaved under.'

At this the town of Mansoul began to prick up its ears. 'And what is it?' they thought. And he said, 'I have something to say to you concerning your King, concerning his law, and also about yourselves. Concerning your King, I know he is great and powerful; but still, all that he has said to you is neither true, nor yet for your advantage.

'1. It is not true; for that which he has hitherto awed you with will not come to pass, even if you do the thing he has forbidden. But if there was danger, what a slavery it is to live always in fear of the greatest of punishment for doing so small and trivial a thing as eating a little fruit!

'2. Concerning his laws, I say this: they are unreasonable,

intricate, and intolerable. Unreasonable, as was hinted before, for the punishment is not proportionate to the offence: there is a great difference and disproportion between life and an apple; yet the one must go for the other, by the law of your Shaddai. But it is also intricate, in that he says, first of all, you may eat of *all*; and yet, afterwards forbids the eating of *one*. And then, in the last place, it must be intolerable, for that fruit which you are forbidden to eat (if you are forbidden any) is that, and that alone, which is able to benefit you in ways you do not yet know, when you eat it. This is clear from the very name of the tree: it is called the Tree of Knowledge of Good and Evil: and do you have that knowledge yet? No, no; nor can you conceive how good it is, how pleasant, and how much to be desired to make people wise, so long as you stand by your King's commandment. Why should you be held in ignorance and blindness? Why should you not be enlarged in knowledge and understanding? And now, inhabitants of the town of Mansoul, to speak more particularly to yourselves, you are not a free people. You are kept in bondage and slavery, and that by a grievous threat, no reason being given but 'I will have it like this; so it shall be.' And is it not grievous to think about, that that very thing you are forbidden to do, if you did it would give you both wisdom and honour? For then your eye will be opened, and you shall be like gods. Now since it is like that,' he said, 'can you be kept by any prince in more slavery and in greater bondage than you are under today? You are made underlings, and are wrapped up in inconveniences, as I have made plain: for what bondage is greater than to be kept in blindness? Will not reason tell you that it is better to have eyes than to be without them? And that to be at liberty is better than to be shut up in a dark and stinking cave?'

And now, while Diabolus was speaking these words to Mansoul, Tisiphone shot at Captain Resistance, where he stood on the gate, and mortally wounded him in the head, so that he, to the amazement of the townsmen, and the encouragement of Diabolus, fell down dead over the wall. Now when Captain Resistance was dead (and he was the only man of war in the town), poor Mansoul was wholly left without courage, nor had he now any heart to resist: but this was as the devil wanted it. Then Mr Ill-pause, the orator Diabolus had brought with him, stood up and addressed himself to speak to the town of Mansoul. The tenor of his speech here follows:

'Gentlemen, it is my master's happiness that he has this day a quiet and teachable audience; and it is hoped by us, that we shall prevail with you not to reject good advice. My master has a very great love for you, and although he knows very well that he runs the hazard of the anger of King Shaddai, yet love to you will make him do more than that. Nor is there any need to say another word to confirm the truth of what he has said; there is not a word but carries with evidence in itself; the very name of the tree may put an end to all controversy in this matter. I therefore at this time shall only add this advice to you, under and by the leave of my lord (and with that he made Diabolus a very low bow): consider his works; look at the tree, and its promising fruit! Remember also that you still know only a little, and that this is the way to know more: and if your reason is not conquered to accept such good counsel, you are not the men I took you to be.'

But when the townsfolk saw that the tree was good for food, and that it was pleasant to the eye, and a tree to be desired to make people wise, they did as old Ill-pause advised: they took and ate it.

Now this I should have told you before, that even then, when this Ill-pause was making his speech to the townsmen, Lord Innocence (whether by a shot from the giant's camp, or from some qualm that suddenly took him, or whether by the stinking breath of that treacherous villain, old Ill-pause, for that is what I am most apt to think), sank down in the place where he stood, nor could he be brought to life again. Thus these two brave men died:

brave men I call them, for they were the beauty and glory of Mansoul, so long as they lived there: nor did there now remain any more a noble spirit in Mansoul; they all fell down and yielded obedience to Diabolus, and became his slaves and vassals, as you will hear.

Now that these were dead, the rest of the townsfolk, like men that had found a fool's paradise, proved the truth of the giant's words. First, they did as Ill-pause had taught them: they looked, they considered, they were taken with the forbidden fruit, they took it and ate. And having eaten, they became immediately drunk with it; so they opened the gates, both Ear-gate and Eye-gate, and let in Diabolus, with all his bands, quite forgetting their good Shaddai, his law, and the judgments that with solemn threatenings he had pronounced on this breach.

Diabolus, having got in at the gates of the town, marches up to the middle of it to make his conquest as sure as he could; and finding by this time the affections of the people warmly inclining toward him, he thinks it would be best to strike while the iron is hot, and he made this deceiving speech to them:

'Alas, my poor Mansoul! I have done this for you, promoting you to honour and making your liberty great.' Then they all with one consent said to this bramble, 'Reign over us'. So he accepted the motion, and became the king of the town of Mansoul. This being done, the next thing was to give him possession of the castle, and so of the whole strength of the town. So he goes into the castle (it was the one which Shaddai built in Mansoul for his own delight and pleasure); this now became a den for the giant Diabolus. Then he makes a garrison for himself, and strengthens and fortifies it with all sorts of provisions against King Shaddai, or those who might try to regain it for him and those who obeyed him.

This done, but not thinking himself secure enough yet, he next thinks of remodelling the town: and so he does, setting up one person and putting down another at will. So he put out of power the Lord Mayor (whose name was Lord Understanding) and Recorder (whose name was Mr Conscience).

When he had garrisoned himself in the town of Mansoul, and had put down and set up what he thought good, Diabolus took to defacing. Now there was in the market-place of Mansoul, and also upon the gates of the castle, an image of the blessed King Shaddai. This image was so accurately engraved (and it was engraved in gold) that it resembled Shaddai himself more than anything did that was then in the world. This he basely commanded to be defaced, and it was basely done by the hand of Mr No-truth. Diabolus also gave an order that the same Mr No-truth should set up in its place the horrid and formidable image of Diabolus, to the great contempt of the former King, and debasement of his town of Mansoul.

Diabolus made several burgesses and aldermen in Mansoul – Mr Incredulity, Mr Haughty, Mr Swearing, Mr Whoring, Mr Hard-heart, Mr Pitiless, Mr Fury, Mr No-truth, Mr Stand-to-lies, Mr False-peace, Mr Drunkenness, Mr Atheism – thirteen in all. Mr Incredulity is the eldest and Mr Atheism the youngest of the company.

Then Diabolus said, 'It is in vain for us to hope for quarter, for this King knows not how to show it. True, perhaps he, at his first sitting down before us, will talk of, and pretend to mercy, so that he may more easily and with less trouble make himself the master of Mansoul again; so whatever he should say, believe not one syllable or tittle of it, for all such language is but to overcome us; and to make us, while we wallow in our blood, the trophies of his merciless victory. My mind is, therefore, that we resolve to the last man to resist him, and not to believe him on any terms; for our danger will come in at that door. But shall we be flattered out of our lives? I hope you know more of the rudiments of politics than to suffer yourselves to be so pitifully served.

'But suppose he should, if he gets us to yield, save some

of our lives, or the lives of some of those who are underlings in Mansoul, what help will that be to you that are the
chief of the town, especially you whom I have set up, and
whose greatness has been procured by you through your
faithful sticking to me? And suppose again that he should
give quarter to every one of you, be sure he will bring you
into that bondage under which you were captivated
before, or a worse, and then what good will your lives do
you? Will you live with him in pleasure, as you do now?
No, no, you must be bound by laws that will pinch you, and
be made to do what at present is hateful to you. I am for
you, if you are for me; and it is better to die valiantly than
to live like pitiful slaves. But I say, the life of a slave will be
accounted a life too good for Mansoul now: blood, blood,
nothing but blood, is in every blast of Shaddai's trumpet
against poor Mansoul now: pray be concerned, I hear he is
coming up, and stand to your arms, that now, while you
have leisure, I may teach you some feats of war. I have
armour for you, and it is by me; indeed, it is sufficient for
Mansoul from top to toe; nor can you be hurt by what his
force can do, if you keep it well fastened about you. Come
therefore to my castle and welcome, and harness yourselves for the war. There is helmet, breastplate, sword,
shield, and what not, that you will fight like men.

'1. My helmet, otherwise called a headpiece, is in hope of
doing well at last, whatever lives you live. This is what the
people had who said they would have peace though they
walked in the wickedness of their heart, to add drunkenness to thirst (see Deuteronomy 29:19). This is a tested
piece of armour, and while a person can keep it on, no
arrow or sword can hurt him. Keep it on, and you will
ward off many a blow to my Mansoul.

'2. My breastplate is of iron (see Revelation 9:9). I had it
forged in my own country, and all my soldiers are armed
with it. In plain language, it is a hard heart, a heart as hard
as iron, and as much past feeling as a stone. If you get and
keep this, mercy will not win you, nor judgment frighten

you. This therefore is a piece of armour most necessary for all to put on if they hate Shaddai, and want to fight against him under my banner.

'3. My sword is a tongue that is set on fire in hell (see Psalm 57:4; James 3:6). It can bend itself to speak evil of Shaddai, his Son, his ways, and people; use this, it has been tried a thousand times twice over; whoever has it, keeps it and makes use of it as I would have him can never be conquered by my enemy.

'4. My shield is unbelief, or calling into question the truth of the word, or all the sayings that speak of the judgment that Shaddai has appointed for wicked men: use this shield. Many attempts he has made upon it, and sometimes, it is true, it has been bruised; but those who have written about the wars of Emmanuel against my servants have testified that "he could do no mighty work there because of their unbelief" (see Mark 6:5, 6; also Job 15:26; Psalm 76:3). Now, to handle this weapon of mine aright is not to believe things because they are true, whatever sort they are or by whoever they are asserted: if he speaks of judgment, do not care; if he speaks of mercy, do not care; if he promises, if he swears that he would do for Mansoul, if it turns to no hurt, but good, disregard what is said, question the truth of it all; for this is to wield the shield of unbelief aright, and as my servants ought, and do; and he who does otherwise does not love me, nor do I count him anything but an enemy to me.

'5. Another piece of my excellent armour is a dumb and prayerless spirit, a spirit that scorns to cry for mercy, let the danger be never so great; so, Mansoul, be sure to make use of this. What, cry for quarter? Never do that, if you want to be mine; I know you stout men, and I am sure that I have clad you with tested armour, so to cry to Shaddai for mercy should be far from you. Besides all this I have a maul, firebrands, arrows and death, all good hand weapons, which will work.'

After he had thus furnished his men with armour, and

arms, he addressed himself to them in words like these: 'Remember that I am your rightful king, and that you have taken an oath and entered into covenant to be true to me and my cause. I say, remember this and show yourselves stout and valiant men of Mansoul. Remember also the kindness that I have always shown to you, without you asking. I have granted to you external things; so the privileges, grants, immunities, profits and honours with which I have endowed you deserve returns of loyalty, my lion-like men of Mansoul: and what so fit a time to show it, as when others seek to take my dominion over you into their own hands? One word more, and I have done: if we can only stand, and overcome this one shock or brunt, I do not doubt that in a little time all the world will be ours; and when that day comes, my true hearts, I will make you kings, princes, and captains, and what brave days we shall have then!'

Diabolus having thus armed and fore-armed his servants and vassals in Mansoul, against their good and lawful King Shaddai, in the next place he doubles his guards at the gates of the town, and retires to the castle, which was his stronghold: his vassals also, to show their wills and supposed (but ignoble) gallantry, exercise their arms every day, and teach one another feats of war. They also defied their enemies, and sang up the praises of their tyrant; they threatened also what men they would be, if ever things should rise so high as a war between Shaddai and their king.

Now all this time the good King Shaddai was preparing to send an army to recover the town of Mansoul again from the tyranny of their pretended King Diabolus; but he thought it best, at first, not to send them under the leadership of brave Emmanuel his Son, but led by some of his servants, to see first by them the temper of Mansoul and whether by them they would be won to the obedience of their King. The army consisted of more than forty thousand, all true men; for they came from the King's own court and were those of his own choosing.

They came up to Mansoul led by four stout generals, each man being captain of ten thousand men. And these are their names and ensigns: the first was Captain Boanerges; the second was Captain Conviction; the third was Captain Judgment; and the fourth was Captain Execution. These were the captains that Shaddai sent to regain Mansoul. Their missions were, in substance, the same in form – 'Go in my name, with this force, to the miserable town of Mansoul; and when you come there, first offer them conditions of peace, and command them that, casting off the yoke and tyranny of the wicked Diabolus, they return to me their rightful Prince and Lord. Command them also that they cleanse themselves from all that is his in the town of Mansoul. And see that you are satisfied touching the truth of their obedience. Thus, when you have commanded them – if in truth they submit – then do to the uttermost of your power what lies in you to set up for me a garrison in the famous town of Mansoul. Do not hurt the least native that moves or breathes there, if they will submit to me, but treat such people as if they were friends or brothers; for I love all such people, and they will be dear to me.'

Well, before the King's forces had sat down before Mansoul for three days, Captain Boanerges commanded his trumpeter to go down to Ear-gate and there, in the name of the great Shaddai, to summon Mansoul to give audience to the message that he was commanded to deliver to them in his Master's name. So the trumpeter, whose name was Take-heed-what-you-hear, went as he was commanded to Ear-gate, and there sounded his trumpet for a hearing. But none of the people who appeared answered or paid any attention, for so had Diabolus commanded.

In the end Boanerges was resolved to hear their answer, so he sent out his trumpeter again to summon Mansoul. He went and sounded, and the townsmen came up; but they made Ear-gate as sure as they could. Now when they had come up to the top of the wall, Diabolus, who was present, was resolved to answer them by himself but then changing his mind he commanded the then Lord Mayor (Lord Incredulity) to do it, saying, 'My Lord, give these renegades an answer, and speak out that Mansoul may hear and understand you.'

So Incredulity, at Diabolus' command, said, 'Know that neither my Lord Diabolus, nor I his servant, nor yet our brave Mansoul, regards you or your message or the King you say has sent you. We do not fear you, nor will we obey your summons. Our gates we will keep shut against you, our place we will keep you out of, nor will we long allow you to sit down before us. Our people must live in quiet; your appearance disturbs them. Therefore, get up, with bag and baggage, and be gone; or we will let fly from the walls against you.'

Then the town of Mansoul shouted for joy, as if some great advantage had been obtained over the captains by Diabolus and his crew. They also rang the bells and made merry, and danced upon the walls. Diabolus also returned to the castle, and the Lord Mayor and Recorder to their places. But the Lord Will-be-will took special care that the gates should be secured with double guards, double bolts and double locks and bars – and that Ear-gate especially be looked to (for that was the gate at which the King's forces most sought to enter in). Lord Will-be-will made old Mr Prejudice, an angry and ill-conditioned fellow, Captain of the Ward at that gate.

Now when the captains heard the answer of the great ones, and they could not get a hearing from the old natives of the town, and that Mansoul was resolved to give the King's army battle, they prepared themselves to try it out by the power of the arm.

Now Mansoul could not sleep securely as before, nor could they go to their debaucheries with that quietness as in times past; for they had from the camp of Shaddai such frequent, warm and terrible alarms – indeed, alarms upon alarms, first at one gate and then at another, and again at all the gates at once — that they were broken as to former peace. Indeed, they had their alarms so frequently — and that when the nights were at longest, the weather coldest, and consequently the season most unseasonable — that that winter was to Mansoul a winter by itself. Sometimes the trumpets would sound, and sometimes the slings would whirl the stones into the town. Sometimes ten thousand of the King's soldiers would be running round the walls of Mansoul at midnight, shouting and lifting up the voice for the battle. Sometimes, again, some of them in the town would be wounded, and their cry and lamentable voice would be heard, to the great molestation of the now languishing town of Mansoul. Indeed, so distressed were they with those that laid that siege against them that I dare say Diabolus their king had his rest much broken in those days.

The captains gathered together to have free conference among themselves, to know what was to be done to gain the town, and agreed that a petition should forthwith be drawn up and sent away to Shaddai with speed. The contents of the petition were thus: 'We have done as we could, yet Mansoul remains in a state of rebellion against you. Now, King of kings, please pardon the unsuccessfulness of your servants. And send, Lord, as we now desire, more forces to Mansoul, that it may be subdued, and a man to head them that the town may both love and fear.'

Wherefore the King called to him Emmanuel his Son, who said, 'Here am I, my Father'. Then said the King, 'You know, as I do myself, the condition of Mansoul and what we have planned. Therefore, my Son, prepare for the war; for you shall go to my camp at Mansoul. You will also prosper and prevail there, and conquer the town of Mansoul.'

Then the King's Son said, 'Your law is in my heart; I delight to do your will. This is the day I have longed for, and the work I have waited for all this while.'

Well, you see how I have told you that the King's Son was engaged to come from the court to save Mansoul, and that his Father had made him Captain of the forces. He now took with him five noble captains and their forces. The first was the noble Captain Credence. His were the red colours, and Mr Promise bore them. The second was that famous captain, Captain Good-hope. His were the blue colours. His standard-bearer was Mr Expectation. The third was that valiant captain, Captain Charity. His standard-bearer was Mr Pitiful. His were the green colours. The fourth was that gallant commander, Captain Innocent. His standard-bearer was Mr Harmless. His were the white colours. The fifth was the truly loyal and well-beloved captain, Captain Patience. His standard-bearer was Mr Suffer-long. His were the black colours.

So the brave Prince took his march to go to the town of Mansoul. Captain Credence led the van, and Captain Patience brought up the rear. So the other three with their men made up the main body, the Prince himself riding in his chariot at the head of them. But when they set out for their march, oh, how the trumpets sounded, their armour glittered, and how the colours waved in the wind! The Prince's armour was all gold, and it shone like the sun in the firmament. The captains' armour was of proof, and was in appearance like the glittering stars. Then they took their journey to go to the town of Mansoul. And unto Mansoul they came.

Now when the town of Mansoul saw the multitude, and the soldiers that were come up against the place, and the battering rams and slings, and the mounts on which they were planted, together with the glittering of their armour and the waving of their colours, they were forced to shift and shift, and again to shift their thoughts. But they hardly changed for thoughts more stout, but rather for thoughts more faint; for though before they thought themselves sufficiently guarded, yet now they began to think that no man knew what would be their lot.

When the good Prince Emmanuel had thus beleaguered Mansoul, in the first place he hands out the white flag, which he caused to be set up among the golden slings that were planted upon Mount Gracious. And this he did for two reasons – to give notice to Mansoul that he could and would yet be gracious, if they turned to him; and that he might leave them the more without excuse, should he destroy them because they continued in their rebellion.

So the white flag with the three golden doves on it was hung out for two days together, to give them time to consider. But they, as if they were unconcerned, made no reply to the favourable signal of the Prince. Then he commanded, and they set the red flag upon that mount called Justice. It was the red flag of Captain Judgment, whose scutcheon was the burning fiery furnace. And this also stood before them waving in the wind for several days together. But just as they carried on under the white flag when that was hung out, so did they also when the red one was. And yet he took no advantage of them.

Then he again commanded that his servants should hand out the black flag of defiance against them, whose scutcheon was the three burning thunderbolts. But Mansoul was as unconcerned at this as at those that went before. Therefore he sent to the town of Mansoul to let them know what he meant by those signs and ceremonies of the flag.

After the town had carried this news to Diabolus and had told him, moreover, that the Prince that lay in the league without the wall waited upon them for an answer, he refused, and huffed as well as he could; but in heart he was afraid. Then he said, 'I will go down to the gates myself, and give him such answer as I think fit.' So he went down to Mouth-gate, and there addressed himself to Emmanuel, but in such language as the town understood not.

'And now,' said the golden-headed Prince, 'I have a word to the town of Mansoul.' So he proceeded, and said:

'O unhappy town of Mansoul! I cannot but be touched with pity and compassion for you. You have accepted Diabolus for your king, and have become a nurse and minister of Diabolonians against your sovereign Lord. Your gates you have opened to him, you have shut them fast against me; you have given him a hearing, but have stopped your ears at my cry. He brought your destruction, and you received both him and it. I have come to you bringing salvation, but you disregard me. What shall I do to you? Listen, therefore — listen to my word, and you shall live. I am merciful, Mansoul, and you will find me so. Do not shut me out of your gates.'

This speech was intended chiefly for Mansoul, but Mansoul would not have the hearing of it. They shut up Ear-gate, they barricaded it up, they kept it locked and bolted. They set a guard at it, and commanded that no Mansoul-ian should go out to him, nor that any from the camp should be admitted into the town. All this they did; so horribly had Diabolus enchanted them to do, and seek to do, for him against their rightful Lord and Prince. Therefore no man nor voice nor sound of man that belonged to the glorious host was to come into the town.

So when Emmanuel saw that Mansoul was thus involved in sin, he calls his army together (since now also his words were despised) and gave out a commandment throughout all his host to be ready against the time appointed. Now, as there was no way lawfully to take the town of Mansoul but to get in by the gates, and at Ear-gate as the chief, therefore he commanded his captains and commanders to bring their battering rams, their slings and their men, and place them at Eye-gate and Ear-gate in order to take the town.

Then he bid that the word should be given out; and the word was at that time 'Emmanuel'. Then was an alarm sounded, and the battering rams were played, and the slings did whirl stones into the town. And thus the battle began.

After three or four notable charges by the Prince and his

noble Captains, Ear-gate was broken open, and the bars
and bolts with which it used to be fast shut up against the
Prince were broken into a thousand pieces. Then the
Prince's trumpets sounded, the captains shouted, the town
shook, and Diabolus retreated to his hold. Well, when the
Prince's forces had broken open the gate, himself came up,
and set his throne in it. Also he set up his standard on a
mount that his men had thrown up to place the mighty
slings on. The mount was called Mount Hear-well. There
the Prince remained, hard by the going in at the gate. He
commanded also that the golden slings should still be
played on the town, especially against the castle, because
that was where Diabolus had retreated for shelter.

Now from Ear-gate the street was straight, right to the
house of Mr Recorder (the one who was Recorder before
Diabolus took the town); and hard by his house stood the
castle, which Diabolus for a long time had made his dis-
gusting den. The captains, therefore, quickly cleared that
street by the use of their slings, so that way was made up to
the heart of the town. Marching in with flying colours, they
came up to the Recorder's house; and that was almost as
strong as was the castle. They also took battering rams with
them to plant against the castle gates. When they came to
the house of Mr Conscience, they knocked and demanded
entrance. Now the old gentleman, not knowing as yet fully
their design, kept his gate shut all the time of this fight.
Therefore Boanerges demanded entrance at his gates;
and since there was no answer, he gave it one stroke with
the head of a ram. And this made the old gentleman
shake, and his house to tremble and totter. Then Mr
Recorder came down to the gate; and with quivering lips
he asked who was there. Boanerges answered, 'We are the
captains and commanders of the great Shaddai and of the
blessed Emmanuel his Son; and we demand possession of
your house for the use of our noble Prince.' And with that
the battering ram gave the gate another shake. This made
the old gentleman tremble all the more; he dared not do

anything but open the gate. Then the King's forces marched in.

Now, all this while, the captains that were in the Recorder's house were playing with the battering rams at the gates of the castle to beat them down. So, after some time and labour, the gate of the castle that was called impregnable was beaten down and broken into splinters; and so a way was made to go up to the hold in which Diabolus had hidden himself. Then tidings were sent down to Ear-gate (for Emmanuel still remained there) to let him know that a way was made in at the gates of the castle of Mansoul. But oh, how the trumpets sounded throughout the Prince's camp now that the war was so nearly ended, and Mansoul itself so near to being set free!

Then the Prince arose from the place where he was, and took with him such of his men of war as were fittest for that expedition, and marched up the street of Mansoul. Now, when he came to the castle gates, he commanded Diabolus to appear, and to surrender himself into his hands. But oh, how loath was the beast to appear! How he shrank! How he cringed! Yet out he came to the Prince.

Then Emmanuel commanded, and they took Diabolus and bound him fast in chains, the better to reserve him for the judgment that he had appointed for him. When Emmanuel had taken him he led him into the market-place, and there before Mansoul stripped him of his armour in which he boasted so much before. And all the while that the giant was being stripped, the trumpets of the golden Prince sounded aloud. The captains also shouted, and the soldiers sang for joy.

But you cannot think (unless you had been there, as I was) what a shout there was in Emmanuel's camp when they saw the tyrant bound by the hand of their noble Prince and tied to his chariot wheels. Those also who rode as volunteers and that came down to see the battle, they shouted with that greatness of voice, and sang with such melodious notes, that they caused those who live in the highest orbs to open their windows, put out their heads, and look down to see the cause of that glory. The townsmen also – as many of them as saw this sight – were, as it were, betwixt the earth and the heavens while they looked. True, they could not tell what would be the issue of things as to them; but all things were done in such excellent methods (and I cannot tell how); but things in the management of them seemed to cast a smile towards the town; so that their eyes, their heads, their hearts and their minds, and all that they had, were taken and held while they observed Emmanuel's order.

So, when the brave Prince had finished his triumph over Diabolus his foe, he turned him up in the midst of his contempt and shame, having given him a charge no more to be a possessor of Mansoul. Then he left Emmanuel, and his camp, to inherit the parched places in a salt land, seeking rest but finding none.

When Diabolus had first taken possession of the town of Mansoul, he brought with him a great number of Diabolonians, men of his own conditions. Now among these was one whose name was Mr Self-conceit; and he was as notable brisk a man as any that in those days possessed the town of Mansoul. Diabolus, then perceiving this man to be active and bold, sent him upon many desperate designs, which he managed better, and more to the pleasing of his lord, than most that came with him from the dens could do. Finding him so fit for his purpose, he promoted him, and made him next to the great Lord Will-be-will. Now Lord Will-be-will, being in those days very well pleased to him and with his achievements, gave him his daughter, Lady Fear-nothing, to wife. Now Mr Self-conceit and Lady Fear-nothing had a child, Mr Carnal-security. There being then in Mansoul those strange kind of mixtures, it was hard for them in some cases to find out who were natives, who not; for Mr Carnal-security sprang from Lord Will-be-will by his mother's side, thoug he had for his father a Diabolonian by nature.

Well, this Carnal-security took much after his father and mother: he was self-conceited, he feared nothing; he was also a very busy man: nothing of news, nothing of doctrine, nothing of alteration or talk of alteration could at any time be on foot in Mansoul but Mr Carnal-security would be at the head or tail of it. But to be sure he would decline those that he deemed the weakest, and always stood with them in his way of standing, that he supposed was the strongest side.

Now when Shaddai the mighty, and Emmanuel his Son, made war upon Mansoul to take it, this Mr Carnal-security was then in the town, and was a great doer among the people, encouraging them in their rebellion, and putting them upon hardening themselves in their resisting the King's forces; but when he saw that the town of Mansoul was taken and converted to the use of the glorious Prince Emmanuel, and when he also saw what was become of Diabolus, and how he was unroofed and made to quit the castle in the greatest contempt and scorn: and that the town of Mansoul was well lined with captains, engines of war, and men, and also provisions; what does he do but wheel about and, as he had served Diabolus against the good Prince, so he feigned that he would serve the Prince against his foes; and having got some little smattering of Emannuel's things by the end, being bold, he ventures himself into the company of the townsmen, and attempts also to chat among them. Now he knew that the power and strength of the town of Mansoul was great, and that it could not but be pleasing to the people if he cried up their might and glory; wherefore he begins his tale with the power and strength of Mansoul, and affirms that it was impregnable; now magnifying the captains, and their slings, and their battering rams; then crying up their fortifications and strongholds; and lastly, the assurance that they had from their Prince that Mansoul should be happy for ever. But when he saw that some of the men of the town were tickled and taken with this discourse, he makes it his business, and, walking from street to street, house to house, and man to man, he brought also Mansoul to dance after his pipe, and to grow almost as carnally secure as himself; so from talking, they went to feasting, and from feasting to sporting, and so to some other matters. Now Emmanuel was still in the town of Mansoul, and he wisely observed their doing. The Lord Mayor, Lord Will-be-will, and the Recorder were also taken with the words of this tattling Diabolonian gentleman, forgetting that their Prince had given them warning before, to take heed that they were not beguiled with any Diabolonian sleight; he had further told them that the security of the now flourishing town of Mansoul did not so much lie in her present fortifications and force as in her so using of what she had as might oblige her Emmanuel to remain within her castle. For the right doctrine of Emmanuel was that the town of Mansoul should take heed that they forget not his Father's love and his; also that they should so demean themselves as to continue to keep themselves in it. Now this was not the way to do it, namely, to fall in love with one of the Diabolonians, and with such a one too as Mr Carnal-security was, and to be led up and down by the nose by him: they should have heard their Prince, and have stoned this naughty pack to death, and taken care to have walked in the ways of their Prince's prescribing; for then their peace would have been as a river, when their righteousness had been like the waves of the sea.

Now when Emmanuel perceived that through the policy of Mr Carnal-security the hearts of the men of Mansoul were chilled and abated in their practical love to him:

First he bemoans them, and bewails their state with the secretary, saying, 'O that my people had listened to me, and that Mansoul had walked in my ways! I would have fed them with the finest of the wheat, and with honey out of the rock I would have sustained them.' This done, he said in his heart, 'I will return to the court, and go to my place, till Mansoul consider and acknowledge their offence.' And he did so, and the cause and manner of his going away from them was thus, for that Mansoul declined him, as manifested in these particulars:

1. They left off their former way of visiting him – they did not come to his royal palace as before.

2. They did not take any notice of whether he came to visit them or not.

3. The love-feasts that had been between their Prince and them, though he still made them, and called them to them, yet they neglected to come to them, or be delighted with them.

4. They did not wait for his counsel, but began to be headstrong and confident in themselves, concluding that now they were strong and invincible, and Mansoul was secure, and beyond all reach of the foe, and that her state must be unalterable for ever.

Now, as was said, Emmanuel perceived that by the craft of Mr Carnal-security the town of Mansoul was taken off from her dependence upon him, and upon his Father by him, and set upon what by them was bestowed upon it; he, at first, as I said, bemoaned their state; then he used means to make them understand that the way they went on in was dangerous: for he sent the Lord High Secretary to them, to forbid them such ways; but twice when he came to them he found them at dinner in Mr Carnal-security's parlour; and perceiving also that they were not willing to reason about matters concerning their good, he took grief, and went his way. When he told this to the Prince Emmanuel, he was grieved also, and returned to his Father's court.

Then Lucifer said: 'Let us withdraw our force from Mansoul; let us do this, and let us terrify them no more, either with summonses or threats, or with the noise of our drum, or any other awakening means. Only let us lie in the field at a distance, and be as if we regarded them not (for frights I see do but awaken them, and make them stand more to their arms). I have also another stratagem in my head: you know Mansoul is a market-town, a town that delights in commerce! What therefore if some of our Diabolonians shall feign themselves foreigners, and go out and bring to the market of Mansoul some of our wares to sell; and what matter at what rates they sell their wares, though it be but for half their worth! Now let those that thus trade in their market be those that are intelligent and true to us, and I will lay down my crown to pawn, it will work. There are two that are come to my thoughts already, that I think will be arch at this work – they are Mr Penny-wise-pound-foolish and Mr Get-i'-th'-hundred-and-lose-i'-th'-shire; nor is this man with the long name at all inferior to the other. What also if you join with them Mr Sweet-world, and Mr Present-good? They are clever, but our true friends and helpers. Let these with as many more engage in this business for us, and let Mansoul be taken up in much business; let them grow full and rich, and this is the way to get the ground of them. Remember that this was how we prevailed upon Laodicea, and how many at present we hold in this snare! Now when they begin to grow full, they will forget their misery; and, if we do not frighten them, they may fall asleep and so be got to neglect their town-watch, their castle-watch, and their watch at the gates.

'Indeed, may we not by this means so encumber Mansoul with abundance that they are forced to make their castle into a warehouse instead of a garrison fortified against us? If we get our goods and commodities there, I reckon the castle is more than half ours. Besides, if we so order it that they are filled with such kind of wares, then if we made a sudden assault upon them it would be hard for the captains to take a shelter there. Do you know the words of the parable (Luke 8:14)? "The deceitfulness of riches chokes the work." And again, "When the heart is over-charged with surfeiting and drunkenness, and the cares of this life, all mischief comes upon them unawares" (Luke 21:34).

'Furthermore, my lords, you very well know that it is not

easy for people to be filled with our things and not to have some of our Diabolonians as retainers to their houses and services. Where is a Mansoulian that is full of this world, that has not for his servants and waiting-men Mr Profuse, or Mr Prodigality, or some others of our Diabolonian gang, such as Mr Voluptuousness, Mr Pragmatical, Mr Ostentation, or the like? Now these can take the castle of Mansoul, or blow it up, or make it unfit for a garrison for Emmanuel, and any of these will do. Indeed, these, for aught I know, may do it for us sooner than an army of twenty thousand men. Therefore, to end as I began, my advice is that we quietly withdraw ourselves, not offering any further force or forcible attempt upon the castle, at least at this time, and let us set on foot our new project, and let us see if that will not make them destroy themselves.'

This advice was highly applauded by them all, and was accounted the very masterpiece of hell, to wit, to choke Mansoul with a fullness of this world, and to surfeit her heart with its good things. But see how things meet together. Just as this Diabolonian council broke up, Captain Credence received a letter from Emmanuel, the contents of which were that on the third day he would meet him in the field, in the plains around Mansoul. 'Meet me in the field!' said the captain. 'What does my Lord mean by this? I know not what he means, meeting me in the field.' So he took the note in his hand, and carried it to the Lord Secretary, to ask his thoughts on it (for this lord was a seer in all matters concerning the King, and also for the good and comfort of the town of Mansoul). So he showed him the note, and desired his opinion of it. 'For my part,' said Captain Credence, 'I do not know what it means.'

So the Lord Secretary read it, and after little pause he said, 'The Diabolonians have had a great consultation today about Mansoul: they have, I dare say, been contriving the utter ruin of the town; and the result of their counsel is to set Mansoul into such a way which, if taken, will surely make her destroy herself. And to this end they are making ready for their own departure out of the town, intending to betake themselves to field again, and there to lie till they see whether this their project will work or not. But you be ready with the men of your Lord, for on the third day they will be in the plain, there to fall upon the Diabolonians; for the Prince will by that time be in the field – indeed, by daybreak, sunrise, or before – and he will have a mighty force against them. So he will be in front of them, and you will be behind them, and between you both their army will be destroyed.

When Captain Credence heard this, he went away to the rest of the captains, and told them what a note he had a while since received from the hand of Emmanuel. And, he said, 'My Lord Secretary has expounded to me what was obscure in it.' He told them, moreover, what must be done by himself and by them to answer the mind of their Lord. Then the captains were glad, and Captain Credence commanded that all the King's trumpeters should ascend on the battlements of the castle, and there in the hearing of Diabolus and of the whole town of Mansoul make the best music that heart could invent. The trumpeters then did as they were commanded: they got themselves up to the top of the castle, and thus they began to sound. Then Diabolus started, and said, 'What can be the meaning of this? They neither sound Boot-and-saddle, nor Horse-and-away, nor a charge. What do these madmen mean, being so merry and glad?' Then one of them answered him, and said: 'This is for joy that their Prince Emmanuel is coming to relieve the town of Mansoul; that to this end he is at the head of an army, and that this relief is near.'

The men of Mansoul also were greatly concerned at this melodious charm of the trumpets; they said to each other, 'Surely this can be no harm to us.' Then the Diabolonians said, 'What had we best do?' And it was answered it was best to quit the town. 'And that,' said one, 'you may do in pursuance of your last counsel, and by so doing also be better able to give the enemy battle, should an army from without come upon us.' So on the second day they withdrew from Mansoul, and stayed in the plains without: but they encamped before Ear-gate, in what terrible manner they could. The reason why they could not stay in the town (besides the reasons that were debated in their recent council) was that they were not possessed of the stronghold, and because, they said, 'We shall find it more convenient for fighting, and also for flying, if need be, when we are encamped in the open.' Besides, the town would have been a pit for them, rather than a place of defence, had the Prince come up and enclosed them fast inside. Therefore they betook themselves to the field, that they might also be out of reach of the slings, by which they were much annoyed all the while they were in the town.

Well, the time that the captains were to fall upon the Diabolonians arrived, and they eagerly prepared themselves for action; for Captain Credence had told the captains overnight that they would meet their Prince in the field tomorrow, and this was like oil to a flaming fire; for they had for a long time been at a distance. Therefore they were all the more earnest about this work. So, when the time came, Captain Credence, with the rest of the men of war, drew out their forces before it was day by the sally-port of the town. And being all ready, Captain Credence went up to the head of the army, and gave the word to the rest of the captains, and they to their under-officers and soldiers: 'The sword of the Prince Emmanuel, and the shield of Captain Credence!' (which is in the Mansoulian tongue, 'The word of God and faith'). Then the captains fell in, and began roundly to front and flank and rear Diabolus's camp.

Now they left Captain Experience in the town, because he was ill of his wounds which the Diabolonians had given him in the last fight. But when he perceived that the captains were at it, what does he do but call for his crutches in haste, get up and away to the battle, saying, 'Shall I lie here when my brothers are in the fight, and when Emmanuel the Prince will show himself in the field to his servants?' But when the enemy saw the man come with his crutches, they were daunted yet the more, for they thought, 'What spirit has possessed these Mansoulians, that they fight us upon their crutches?' Well, the captains, as I said, fell in, and bravely handled their weapons, still crying out, and shouting as they laid on blows, 'The sword of the Prince Emmanuel, and the shield of Captain Credence!'

Now when Diabolus saw that the captains had come out, and that they surrounded his men so valiantly, he concluded that for the present nothing was to be expected from them but blows, with the dints of their two-edged swords. So he also fell upon the Prince's army with all his deadly force. Thus the battle was joined. Now who was it that at first Diabolus met with in the fight, but Captain Credence on the one hand, and Lord Will-be-will on the other? Now Will-be-will's blows were like the blows of a giant, for that man had a strong arm, and he fell in upon the Election-Doubters, for they were the lifeguard of Diabolus, and he kept them occupied a good while, cutting and battering shrewdly. Now when Captain Credence saw him engaged , he stoutly on the other hand fell upon the same company also, so they put them to great disorder. Now Captain Good-hope had engaged the Vocation-Doubters, and they were sturdy men; but the captain was a valiant man. Captain Experience also sent him some aid; so he made the Vocation-doubters retreat. The rest of the armies were hotly engaged, and that on every side, and the Diabolonians fought stoutly. Then the Lord Secretary commanded that the slings from the castle should be used, and his men could throw stones at a hair's breadth. But after a while those who fled before the captains of the Prince began to rally again, and they came up stoutly upon the rear of the Prince's army, wherefore the Prince's army began to faint; but remembering they would see the face of their Prince by and by, they took courage, and a very

fierce battle was fought. Then the captains shouted, 'The
sword of the Prince Emmanuel, and the shield of Captain
Credence!', and with that Diabolus gave back, thinking
that more aid had come. But no Emmanuel as yet
appeared. Moreover the battle hung in doubt, and they
made a little retreat on both sides. Now in the time of
respite, Captain Credence bravely encouraged his men to
stand to it, and Diabolus did the same, as well as he could.
But Captain Credence made a brave speech to his soldiers,
the contents of which here follow:

'Gentlemen soldiers, and my brothers in this plan, I
rejoice much to see in the field for our Prince this day so
stout and valiant an army, and faithful lovers of Mansoul.
You have hitherto rightly shown yourselves men of truth
and courage against the Diabolonian forces, so that for all
their boast they have not yet cause to boast much of their
gains. Now take your usual courage and show yourselves
men, just this once; for in a few minutes after the next
engagement this time, you will see our Prince show himself
in the field; for we must make this second assault upon this
tyrant Diabolus, and then Emmanuel is coming.'

No sooner had the captain made this speech to his soldiers than Mr Speedy came post to the captain from the
Prince, to tell him that Emmanuel was at hand. When the
captain had received this news, he communicated it to the
other field officers, and they again to their soldiers and
men of war. Therefore, like men raised from the dead, the
captains and their men arose, went up to the enemy, and
cried as before, 'The sword of the Prince Emmanuel and
the shield of Captain Credence!'

The Diabolonians also bestirred themselves, and made
resistance as well as they could, but in this last engagement
they lost their courage, and many of the Doubters fell
down dead to the ground. Now when they had been in
heat of battle about an hour or more, Captain Credence
lifted up his eyes, and beheld Emmanuel coming, and he
came with colours flying, trumpets sounding, and the feet

of his men scarce touched the ground, so quickly did they hasten towards the captains that were engaged. Then Captain Credence wheeled his men towards the town, and gave Diabolus the field. So Emmanuel came upon him on the one side, and the enemies' place was between them both; then again they fell to it afresh, and a little while afterwards Emmanuel and Captain Credence met, still trampling down the slain as they came.

But when the captains saw that the Prince had come, and that he fell on the Diabolonians on the other side, and that Captain Credence and his Highness had got them between them, they shouted again, 'The sword of Emmanuel, and the shield of Captain Credence!' Now when Diabolus saw that he and his forces were so hard beset by the Prince and his princely army, he and the lords of the pit that were with him made their escape, and deserted their army, and left them to fall by the hand of Emmanuel and of his noble Captain Credence; so they all fell down slain before them, before his Prince and before his royal army: there was not left so much as one Doubter alive; they lay spread upon the ground like dead men, as one would spread dung upon the land.

When the battle was over, all things came in order in the camp; then the captains and elders of Mansoul came together to salute Emmanuel and welcome him, with a thousand welcomes, for he had come to the borders of Mansoul again. So he smiled upon them, and said, 'Peace be unto you'. Then they addressed themselves to go to the town; they went then to go up to Mansoul, they, the Prince, with all the new forces that now he had brought with him to the war. Also all the gates of the town were set open to receive him, so glad were they of his blessed return. And this was the manner and order of his going into Mansoul.

When the town of Mansoul had rid themselves of some of their enemies, and of the troublers of their peace, in the next place a strict commandment was given out that Lord

Will-be-will should still, with his man Diligence, search for and do his best to apprehend such town Diabolonians as were still alive in Mansoul. The names of several of them were Mr Fooling, Mr Let-good-slip, Mr Slavish-fear, Mr No-love, Mr Mistrust, Mr Flesh, and Mr Sloth. It was also commanded that he should apprehend Mr Evil-questioning's children that he left behind him, and that they should demolish his house there; Mr Doubt was his eldest son; the next to him were Legal-life, Unbelief, Wrong-thought-of-Christ, Clip-promise, Carnal-sense, Live-by-feel, and Self-love. All these he had by one wife, and her name was No-hope; she was the kinswoman of old Incredulity, for he was her uncle, and when her father old Dark was dead, he took her and brought her up, and when she was marriage-able, he gave her to this old Evil-questioning to be his wife.

Now Lord Will-be-will put his commission into execution, with great Diligence his man. He took Fooling in the streets, and hanged him up in Want-wit Alley, over against his own house. This Fooling was he that would have had the town of Mansoul deliver up Captain Credence into the hands of Diabolus, provided that then he withdrew his forces out of the town. He also took Mr Let-good-slip one day as he was busy in the market, and executed him according to law. Now there was an honest poor man in Mansoul, and his name was Mr Meditation, and one of no great account in the days of apostasy; but now of repute with the best of the town. This man therefore they were willing to promote. Now Mr Let-good-slip had had a great deal of wealth in Mansoul, and at Emmanuel's coming it was sequestered for the Prince's use; this therefore was now given to Mr Meditation to improve for the common good, and after him to his son Mr Think-well – this Think-well was his son by Mrs Piety his wife, and she was the daughter of Mr Recorder.

After this Lord Will-be-will apprehended Clip-promise; now he was a notorious villain, for by his doings much of the King's coin was clipped and abused, and so he was made a public example. He was arraigned, and sentenced to be set in the pillory first, and then to be whipped by all the children and servants in Mansoul, and then to be hanged till he was dead.

He also apprehended Carnal-sense, and put him in prison; but how it came about I cannot tell, but he escaped, and the bold villain will not yet quit the town, but lurks in the Diabolonian dens and at night haunts honest men's houses like a ghost. Therefore a proclamation was set up in the market-place in Mansoul, signifying that whoever could discover Carnal-sense and apprehend him and slay him would be admitted to the Prince's table daily, and would be made keeper of the treasure of Mansoul. Many therefore tried to do this, but they could not capture him and slay him, though he was often discovered. But Lord Will-be-will took Mr Wrong-thought-of-Christ, and put him in prison, and he died of lingering consumption.

Self-love was also taken and committed to custody, but there were many that were allied to him in Mansoul, so his judgment was deferred; but at last Mr Self-denial stood up and said, 'If such villains as these may be winked at in Mansoul, I will lay down my commission.' He also took him from the crowd and had him among his soldiers, and there he was brained. But some in Mansoul muttered at it, though none dared speak plainly, because Emmanuel was in the town. But this brave act of Captain Self-denial came to the Prince's ears, so he sent for him, and made him a lord in Mansoul. Lord Will-be-will also obtained great commendation from Emmanuel for what he had done for the town of Mansoul.

Then Lord Self-denial took courage, and set to the pursuing of the Diabolonians with Lord Will-be-will; and they took Live-by-feeling, and they took Legal-life, and put them in prison till they died. But Mr Unbelief was a nimble fellow: him they could never lay hold of, though they attempted to do it often. He therefore, and some of the subtlest of the Diabolonians, still remained in Mansoul, to the time that Mansoul left off staying in the kingdom of Universe any longer, but they kept to their dens and holes; if one of them appeared, or happened to be seen in one of the streets in the town of Mansoul, the whole town would be up in arms after them, indeed the very children in Mansoul would cry out after them as after a thief, and would wish that they might stone them to death with stones. And now Mansoul arrived to some good degree of peace and quiet, and her Prince stayed within her borders, and her captains also, and her soldiers did their duties, and Mansoul minded the trade that she had with the country afar off; also she was busy in her manufacture.

When the town of Mansoul had thus far rid themselves of their enemies, and the troublers of their peace, the Prince sent to them and appointed a day when he would meet the whole people at the market-place, and there charge them with future matters, that, if they observed them, would tend to their farther safety and comfort, and to the condemnation and destruction of their home-bred Diabolonians. So the appointed day came, and the townsmen met together. Emmanuel also came down in his chariot, and all his captains in their state attended him on the right hand and on the left. Then there was a call for silence, and after some mutual greetings of love, the Prince began, and said:

'You, my Mansoul, and the beloved of my heart, many and great are the privileges that I have bestowed upon you; I have singled you out from others and have chosen you to myself, not for your worthiness, but for my own sake. I have also redeemed you, not only from the dread of my Father's law, but from the hand of Diabolus. This I have done because I loved you, and because I have set my heart on doing you good. Also, so that everything that might hinder the way to the pleasures of Paradise might be taken out of the way, I have laid down for you, for your soul a plenary satisfaction, and have bought you for myself; a price not of corruptible things, such as silver and gold, but a price of blood, my own blood, which I have freely spilt on the ground to make you mine. So I have reconciled you, Mansoul, to my Father, and entrusted you in the mansion-houses that are with my Father in the royal city, where there are things that no eye has seen, nor has it entered into the heart of man to conceive.

'Besides, you see what I have done, and how I have taken you out of the hand of your enemies. You have deeply revolted from my Father, and were content to be possessed by these enemies, and also to be destroyed. I came to you first by my law, then by my gospel, to awaken you, and show you my glory. And you know what you were, what you said, what you did, and how many times you rebelled against my Father and me; yet I did not leave you, as you see today, but came to you, have borne your manners, have waited upon you and, after all, accepted you purely out of my grace and favour. I would not allow you to be lost, and you would most willingly have been. I also surrounded you, afflicted you on every side, that I might make you weary of your ways, and bring your heart to a willingness to close with your good and happiness. And when I had got a complete conquest over you, I turned it to your advantage.

'You see also what a company of my Father's host I have lodged within your borders, captains and rulers, soldiers, men of war, engines and excellent devices, to subdue and bring down your foes; you know what I mean, Mansoul. And they are my servants and yours too, Mansoul. Indeed, my plan of giving you possession of them, and the natural tendency of each of them, is to defend, purge, strengthen, and sweeten you for myself, Mansoul, and to make you fit for my Father's presence, blessing, and glory. For you are created to be prepared for these.

'Moreover, Mansoul, you see how I have passed by your backslidings, and have healed you. Indeed I was angry with you, but I have turned away my anger, and my indignation is over in the destruction of your enemies. Nor did your goodness bring me back to you, after I had hidden my face because of your transgressions, and withdrawn my presence from you. The way of backsliding was yours, but the way and means of recovery was mine. I invented the means of your return; it is I that made a hedge and a wall, when you were beginning to turn to things in which I took no delight. It was I that made your sweet bitter, your day night, your smooth way thorny, and also confounded all those who sought your destruction. It was I that set Mr Godly-fear to work in Mansoul. It was I that stirred up your conscience and understanding, your will and your affections, after your great and woeful decay. It was I that put life into you to seek me, that you might find me and, in your finding, find your own health, happiness, and salvation. It was I that fetched the Diabolonians out of Mansoul again; it was I that overcame them and destroyed them in front of you.

'And now, Mansoul, I have returned to you in peace, and your transgressions against me are as if they had not been. Nor shall it be with you as in former times, but I will do better for you than at your beginning. For in just a little while, Mansoul, after a few more times have gone over your head, I will take down this famous town of Mansoul stick and stone to the ground. But do not be troubled at what I say. I will carry the stones and timber and walls and dust and inhabitants into my own country, the kingdom of my Father, and there I will set it up in such strength and glory as it never did see in the kingdom where it is now placed. I will set it up there for my Father's habitation, because for that purpose it was at first erected in the kingdom of Universe; and there I will make it a spectacle of wonder, a monument of mercy. There the natives of Mansoul will see all that of which they have seen nothing here; there they will be equal to those to whom they have been inferior here. And there, Mansoul, you will have such communion with me as is not possible to be enjoyed here, nor ever could be, even if you lived in Universe for a thousand years.

'There, Mansoul, you will no longer be afraid of murders or of Diabolonians. There will be no more plots against you. There you will hear no more bad news, or the noise of the Diabolonian drum. There you will not see the Diabolonian standard-bearers, nor yet behold Diabolus's standard. No Diabolonian mount will be cast up against you there, nor will the Diabolonian standard be set up there to make you afraid. There you will meet with no sorrow or grief, nor shall it be possible for any Diabolonian ever again to creep into your skirts, burrow in your walls, or be seen within your borders all the days of eternity. Life there will last longer than here you are able to desire it should, and yet it will always be sweet and new, nor shall any impediment attend it for ever.

'There, Mansoul, you will meet many of those who have been like you, and that have shared your sorrows — those I have chosen and redeemed, and set apart like you for my Father's court and city royal. All of them will be glad in you; and you, when you see them, will be glad in your heart.

'There are things of your Father's providing and mine, Mansoul, which were never seen since the beginning of the world, and they are laid up with my Father, and sealed up among his treasures for you till you come here to them. I told you before that I would remove my Mansoul, and set it up elsewhere; and where I set it, there are those who love you, and those who rejoice in you now, but much more when they see you exalted to honour. My Father will send them for you to fetch you; and their bosoms are chariots to put you in. And you, Mansoul, will ride on the wings of the wind. They will come to convey, conduct and bring you to the place where, when your eyes see more, you will desire to have your haven.

'And thus, Mansoul, I have showed you what will be done to you hereafter, if you can understand; and now I will tell you what at present must be your duty and practice, until I come and fetch you to myself, according as it is related in the scriptures of truth.

'First, you must hereafter keep more white and clean the liveries which I gave you before my last withdrawing from you. They are in themselves fine linen, but you must keep them white and clean. This will be your wisdom, your honour, and will be greatly for my glory. When your garments are white, the world will count you mine. Also when your garments are white, then I am delighted in your ways, for then your goings to and fro will be like a flash of lightning that everyone present must take notice of, and their eyes will be made to dazzle at it. Deck yourself therefore according to my bidding, and make yourself, by my law, straight steps for your feet; then your King will greatly desire your beauty, for he is your Lord, and you must worship him.

'Now that you may keep them as I bid you, I have, as I told you before, provided an open fountain for you to wash your garments in. Therefore, see that you often wash in my fountain, and do not go in defiled garments, for as it is to my dishonour, and my disgrace, so it will be to your discomfort, when you walk in filthy garments. Therefore do not let my garments, your garments that I gave you, be defiled or spotted by the flesh (see Jude 23). Always keep your garments white, and let your head lack no ointment.

'Mansoul, I have often delivered you from the designs, plots, attempts and conspiracies of Diabolus, and for all this I ask nothing but that you do not pay me back evil for my good, but that you bear in mind my love, and the continuation of my kindness to my beloved Mansoul, so as to provoke you to walk, as far as you can, according to the benefit bestowed on you. Of old, the sacrifices were bound with cords to the horns of the golden altar. Consider what is said to you, my blessed Mansoul.

'O my Mansoul, I have lived, I have died; I live, and will die no more for you; I live, that you may not die. Because I live, you will live also. I reconciled you to my Father by the blood of my cross, and being reconciled you will live through me.

'Nothing can hurt you but sin; nothing can grieve me but sin; nothing can make you base before your foes but sin: take heed of sin, Mansoul.

'And do you know why at first I allowed, and do still allow, Diabolonians to live within your walls, Mansoul? It is to keep you waiting, to test your love, to make you watchful, and to cause you to prize my noble captains, their soldiers, and my mercy.

'It is also so that you may be made to remember what a deplorable condition you were once in – I mean when not some but all lived not in your wall but in your castle, and in your stronghold.

'O my Mansoul, if I slayed them all within, there are many without that would bring you into bondage; for if all these within were cut off, those without would find you sleeping, and then as in a moment they would swallow up my Mansoul. I therefore left them in you, not to hurt you (which they will still do if you listen to them, and serve them), but to do you good, which they must, if you watch and fight against them.

'Show me your love, my Mansoul, and do not let those that are within your walls take your affections off from him that has redeemed your soul. Indeed, let the sight of a Diabolonian heighten your love to me. I came once and twice, and three times, to save you from the poison of those arrows that would have brought about your death; stand for me, my friend, my Mansoul, against the Diabolonians, and I will stand for you before my Father, and all his court. Love me against temptation, and I will love you, notwithstanding your weaknesses.

'O my Mansoul, remember what my captains, my soldiers, and my engines have done for you. They have fought for you, they have borne much at your hand to do you good, Mansoul. If you had not had them to help you, Diabolus would certainly have made a hand of you.

Nourish them, therefore, my Mansoul. When you do well, they will be well; when you do wrong, they will be ill, and sick and weak. Do not make my captains sick, Mansoul; for if they are sick, you cannot be well; if they are weak, you cannot be strong; if they are faint, you cannot be stout and valiant for your King. Nor must you expect always to live by sense: you must live on my word. You must believe, O my Mansoul, when I am for you, that I still love and bear you upon my heart for ever.

'Remember therefore, O my Mansoul, that you are loved by me; as I have taught you before to watch, to fight, to pray, and to make war against my foes, so now I command you to believe that my love is constant to you, O my Mansoul. Now I have set my heart and love upon you, watch: "I will not impose any other burden on you: only hold on to what you have until I come"' (Revelation 2:24).

6

The Life and Death of Mr Badman

WISEMAN: Good morning, my good neighbour, Mr Attentive. Where are you walking so early this morning? You look as if you were concerned about something more than ordinary. Have you lost any of your cattle, or what is the matter?

ATTENTIVE: Good morning to you. I have not as yet lost anything, but you guess right; for I am, as you say, concerned in my heart; but it is because of the badness of the times. And you (as all our neighbours know) are a very observant man. What do you think of them?

WISEMAN: Why, I think as you say, they are bad times; and bad they will be until men are better; for they are bad men that make bad times. If men, therefore, would mend, so would the times.

ATTENTIVE: Amen, amen. But why do you sigh so deeply? Is it for anything other than what, as you have seen, I myself am concerned?

WISEMAN: I am concerned with you for the badness of the times; but that was not the cause of that sigh you noticed. I sighed at the remembrance of the death of that man for whom the bell tolled at our town yesterday.

ATTENTIVE: Why, your neighbour Mr Goodman is not dead? I did hear that he had been sick.

WISEMAN: No, no. It is not he. If he had died, I should only have been concerned that the world had lost a light; but the man I am concerned for now was one that never was good – therefore a person who is not only dead, but damned. The man that I mean is a Mr Badman; he has lived in our town a great while.

ATTENTIVE: Tell me what it is that makes you think that Mr Badman has gone to hell.

WISEMAN: I was a man when he was but a boy, and I observed him specially from first to last.

ATTENTIVE: Then let me hear from you an account of his life.

WISEMAN: From a child he was very bad. His very beginning was ominous, and presaged that no good end was likely to follow. There were several sins that he was given to, when he was only little, that showed him to be notoriously affected with original corruption. He used to be, as we say, the ringleader and master-sinner from a child.

ATTENTIVE: Yet these are only generalities. Tell me in particular which were the sins of his childhood.

WISEMAN: I will so. When he was but a child he was so addicted to lying that his parents scarce knew when to believe he was speaking the truth; indeed, he would invent, tell and stick to the lies that he invented and told, and with such an audacious face that one might even read in his very countenance the symptoms of a hard and desperate heart in this way. When a fit or an occasion to lie came upon him, he would invent, tell and stick to his lie as steadfastly as if it had been the biggest of truths that he told, and he did it with that hardening of his heart and face that it would be a wonder to those that stood by.

ATTENTIVE: Truly it was a bad beginning. He served the devil early on.

WISEMAN: You say true. He was also much given to pilfering and stealing. If he could lay hold of anything at a neighbour's house, he would take it away; he took great pleasure in robbing gardens and orchards; indeed, what was his father's could not escape his fingers.

ATTENTIVE: You make me wonder more and more. What, play the thief too! He must have known, though he was only a child, that what he took from others was not his own. Besides, if his father was a good man (as you say), the boy must also have heard from him that to steal was to transgress God's law, and so to run the risk of eternal damnation.

WISEMAN: His father did not fail to use the means to reclaim him, often urging (as I have been told) that saying in the law of Moses, *Thou shalt not steal*. The light of nature also, though he was little, must have shown him that what he took from others was not his own, and that he would not willingly have been treated so himself. But all was to no purpose, let father and conscience say what they would to him, he would go on, he was resolved to go on in his wickedness.

ATTENTIVE: But his father would, as you intimate, sometimes rebuke him for his wickedness. How would he react then?

WISEMAN: How? Why, like a thief that is found out. He would stand gloating, and hanging down his head in a sullen, pouching manner; a body might read (as we used to say) the picture of ill-luck in his face. And when his father demanded his answer to such questions concerning his villainy, he would grumble and mutter at him; and that would be all he could get.

ATTENTIVE: But you said that he would also rob his father. That was an unnatural thing.

WISEMAN: Natural or unnatural, all is one to a thief. Besides, you must think that he had companions to whom he was, for the wickedness that he saw in them, more firmly knit than to either father or mother. What would he have cared if father and mother had died for grief for him? Their death would have been, as he would have counted it, a great release and to him; for the truth is, they and their counsel were his bondage. And if I forget not, I have heard some say that when he was, at times, among his companions he would greatly rejoice to think that his parents were old and could not live long, and then (he said) 'I shall be my own man to do what I like, without their control.'

ATTENTIVE: But can you imagine what it might be that would make him think that this manner of pilfering and stealing was no great matter?

WISEMAN: It was because the things he stole were small – to rob orchards and gardens, and to steal pullen and the like – these he counted tricks of youth; nor would he be beaten out of it by all that his friends could say. They would tell him that he must not covet or desire (and yet to desire is less than to take) even anything, the least thing that was his neighbour's; and that if he did, it would be a transgression of the law. But all was one to him. What through the wicked talk of his companions, and the delusions of his own corrupt heart, he would go on in his pilfering course, and where he thought himself secure, would talk of and laugh at it when he had done.

ATTENTIVE: What other sins was he addicted to?

WISEMAN: He could not endure the Lord's Day, because of the holiness that went with it. The beginning of that day was to him as if he was going to prison, unless he could get out from his father and mother and lurk among his companions until holy duties were over. He was greatly given, even while a lad, to grievous swearing and cursing. He counted it a glory to swear and curse.

ATTENTIVE: Oh, what a young villain was this! But, since this young Badman would not be ruled at home, his father should have tried what good could have been done elsewhere by putting him out to some man of his acquaintance.

WISEMAN: Alas! His father did so. He put him out to one of his acquaintance, and entreated him of all love that he would take care of his son, and keep him from extravagant ways. His trade also was honest and handy. Besides, he was fully occupied in it, so that this young Badman had no vacant times or idle hours given him by his calling, when he might take opportunities to behave badly. But all was one to him. As he had begun to be vile in his father's house, so he continued to be when he was in the house of his master. His master was a very good man, a very devout person. He was also a man very meek and merciful, one that did never over-drive young Badman in business, nor that kept him at it at unreasonable hours.

ATTENTIVE: That is rare. I for my part can see few that can parallel Mr Badman's master in these things.

WISEMAN: Nor I neither. For the most part masters nowadays are such as mind nothing but their worldly concerns. Indeed, I much fear that there have been many promising lads put out by their parents to such masters, who have quite undone them as to the next world.

ATTENTIVE: More's the pity.

WISEMAN: Then I will tell you that he had not been with his master much more than a year and a half when he became acquainted with three young villains who taught him to add to his sin much of the same kind, and he received their instructions aptly. One of them was chiefly given to uncleanness, another to drunkenness, and the third to purloining or stealing from his master. He did as they did. He became a frequenter of taverns and tippling-houses, and would stay there until he was as drunk as a beast. And if he could not get out by day, he would, be sure, get out by night. He was a ringleader to them all in the beastly sin of whoredom. He was also best acquainted with such houses where they were, and so could readily lead the rest of his gang to them.

ATTENTIVE: That is a deadly thing to young men. It is a dreadful thing to live and die in this transgression.

WISEMAN: True. I heard of one that would say to his miss, when he tempted her to commit this sin, 'If you will venture your body, I will venture my soul.' And I myself heard another say, when he was tempting a maid to commit uncleanness with him — it was in Oliver Cromwell's days — that if she proved to be with child he would tell her how she might escape punishment – and that was then somewhat severe: 'Say,' he told her, 'when you come before the judge, that you are with child by the Holy Ghost.' I heard him say this, and it greatly affected me.

ATTENTIVE: It is the most horrible thing that ever I heard in my life. These are notable stories indeed.

WISEMAN: So they are, and as true as notable.

ATTENTIVE: Well, but I wonder, if young Badman's master knew him to be such a wretch, that he would allow him in his house.

WISEMAN: Badman ran away from him once or twice, and would not at all be ruled. So the next time he ran away from him, he let him go indeed.

ATTENTIVE: And did the old man give him money to set up with?

WISEMAN: Yes, his father did give him a piece of money, and he did set up, and almost as soon set down again; for he was not long set up before by his ill managing of his matters at home, together with his extravagant expenses elsewhere, he got so far into debt, and had so little in his shop to pay, that he was hard put to it to keep himself out of prison. But when his creditors understood that he was about to marry and in a fair way to get a rich wife, they said among themselves, 'We will not be hasty with him – if he gets a rich wife, he will pay us all.'

He was looking out for a rich wife – a wife he wanted, or rather money – as for a woman, he could have whores enough at his whistle. But there dwelt a maid not far from him that was both godly and one that had a good portion; but how to get her, there lay all the craft. Well, he calls a council of some of his most trusty and cunning companions, and shares his thoughts with them. Said he, 'How shall I accomplish my end? She is religious, and I am not.' Then one of them replied, 'Since she is religious, you must pretend to be so too.'

ATTENTIVE: Did he take this counsel?

WISEMAN: Did he! Yes, and to be short, in little time Mr Badman obtained his desire, got this honest girl and her money, was married to her, brought her home, made a feast, entertained her royally. But her portion had to pay for everything.

ATTENTIVE: This beginning was bad, and yet I fear it was but the beginning of bad.

WISEMAN: You may be sure that it was but the beginning of badness, for other evils came on apace. Now the poor woman saw that she was betrayed indeed; now also his old companions began to flock about him and to haunt his house and shop as formerly. In little time he drove all good company from her, and made her sit alone. He also began now to go out at night to those who were his friends before, with whom he would stay sometimes till midnight, and sometimes till almost morning, and then come home as drunk as a swine. And this was the course of Mr Badman.

ATTENTIVE: Was his calling so profitable to him as always to keep his purse's belly full, though he was himself a great spender?

WISEMAN: No, it was not his trade that did it, though he had a pretty trade too. He had another way to get money. He had the knack of going bankrupt, and getting hatfuls of money by it.

ATTENTIVE: What do you mean?

WISEMAN: I speak plainly. Once he gives a great and sudden rush into several men's debts, to the value of about four or five thousand pounds. Well, when Mr Badman had well feathered his nest with other men's goods and money, after a little time he goes bankrupt. And by and by it was spread about that Mr Badman had shut up shop, was gone, and could trade no longer. Now by the time his breaking came to his creditors' ears, he had by craft and knavery made so sure of what he had that his creditors could not touch a penny. Well, when he had finished, he sends his mournful sugared letters to his creditors, to let them understand what had happened to him, and desired them not to be severe with him; for he bore towards all men an honest mind, and would pay so far as he was able. His creditors, by great efforts, obtained five shillings in the pound.

ATTENTIVE: Why, this was a mere cheat.

WISEMAN: It was a cheat indeed. This way of going bankrupt is nothing else but a neater way of thieving, of picking pockets, of breaking into shops and taking from men what one has nothing to do with.

ATTENTIVE: What a wicked man this was! This argues that Mr Badman had but little conscience.

WISEMAN: This argued that Mr Badman had no conscience at all; for conscience, the least spark of conscience, cannot endure this.

ATTENTIVE: Well, now I have heard enough of Mr Badman's naughtiness. Go on to his death.

WISEMAN: The sun is not so low! We have three hours to night yet.

ATTENTIVE: I am not in any great haste; but I thought you had done with his life now.

WISEMAN: Done! No, I have much more to say yet.

ATTENTIVE: Then he has much more wickedness than I thought he had.

WISEMAN: That may be. But let us proceed. If he should get anything by the end that had a scandal in it, if it just touched on 'believers', however falsely so called, then he would glory, laugh and be glad, and lay it upon the whole party, saying, 'Hang them rogues! There is not a barrel better herring of all the holy brotherhood of them. *Like to like, said the Devil to the collier* – this is your precise crew.'

ATTENTIVE: If those that make profession of religion are wise, Mr Badman's watchings and words will make them the more wary and careful in all things.

WISEMAN: You say true. For when we see men watch for our halting, and rejoice to see us stumble and fall, it should make us so much more careful. I think it was as delightful to Mr Badman to hear, raise and tell lies and lying stories of them that fear the Lord as it was for him to go to bed when he was weary. This Mr Badman added to all his wickedness this – that he was a very proud man, a very proud man. He was exceeding proud and haughty in mind; he looked that what he said ought not, must not, be contradicted or opposed. He counted himself as wise as the wisest in the country, as good as the best, and as beautiful as he that had most of it. He took great delight in praising himself, and as much in the praises that others gave him. He could not abide anyone to think themselves above him, or that their wit or personage should by others be set before his. And this Mr Badman was so envious that he would swell with it like a toad (as we say) swells with poison. His envy was so rank and strong that if at any time it turned its head against a man, it would hardly ever be pulled in again. He would watch over that man to do him mischief, as the cat watches over the mouse to destroy it; indeed, he would wait seven years, but he would have an opportunity to hurt him.

ATTENTIVE: But this is a rare case, this of Mr Badman, that he should never in all his life be touched with remorse.

WISEMAN: Remorse I cannot say he ever had, if by remorse you mean repentance for his evils. Yet twice I remember he was under some trouble of mind about his condition. Once when he broke his leg as he came home drunk from the alehouse; and another time when he fell sick and thought he was going to die. For not many months after his leg was well he had a very dangerous fit of sickness, insomuch that now he began to think he must die indeed.

ATTENTIVE: Well, and what did he think and do then?

WISEMAN: He thought he must go to hell. This I know, for he could not forbear to say so. To my best remembrance, he lay crying out all one night for fear; and at times he would so tremble that he would make the very bed shake under him. But oh, how the thoughts of death, of hell-fire and of eternal judgment did then rack his conscience! Fear might be seen in his face and in his tossings to and fro; it might also be heard in his words and be understood by his heavy groans. He would often cry, 'I am undone, I am undone – my vile life has undone me!'

ATTENTIVE: How was he when he drew to his end – how was he when he was (as we say) at the grave's mouth?

WISEMAN: Why, there was not any other alteration in him than was made by his disease upon his body. His mind was the same, his heart was the same. He was the selfsame Mr Badman still.

ATTENTIVE: How was he in his death? Was death strong upon him, or did he die with ease, quietly?

WISEMAN: As quietly as a lamb. There seemed not to be in it, to standers by, so much as a strong struggle of nature. And as for his mind, it seemed to be wholly at quiet. But why do you ask such a question?

ATTENTIVE: Not for my own sake, but for others. For there is such an opinion as this among the ignorant – that if a man dies (as they call it) like a lamb, that is, quietly and without that consternation of mind that others show in their death, they conclude (and beyond all doubt) that such a person has gone to heaven.

WISEMAN: There is no judgment to be made by a quiet death. Suppose that one man should die quietly, another should die suddenly and a third should die under great consternation of spirit, no man can judge their eternal condition by the manner of any of these kinds of deaths. But Mr Badman was naught – his life was evil, his ways were evil, however quietly he died.

ATTENTIVE: Well, I see that the sun is getting low and you have come to a conclusion with Mr Badman's life and death; therefore I will take my leave of you. Only first, let me tell you I am glad that I have met you today and that we talked of Mr Badman's state. I also thank you for your freedom with me in granting your reply to all my questions. I would only beg our prayers that God will give me such grace that I may neither live nor die as Mr Badman did.

7

Verse

He that is down needs fear no fall,
   He that is low no pride;
He that is humble ever shall
   Have God to be his guide.
I am content with what I have,
   Little be it or much;
And, Lord, contentment still I crave,
   Because thou savest such.
Fulness to such a burden is
   That go on pilgrimage:
Here little, and hereafter bliss,
   Is best from age to age.

          (From *The Pilgrim's Progress* Part II. It is
          the shepherd boy's song, which Mr
          Greatheart advises us to listen to.)

Who would true valour see,
   Let him come hither;
One here will constant be,
   Come wind, come weather.
There's no discouragement
   Shall make him once relent

His first avow'd intent
   To be a pilgrim.

Whoso beset him round
   With dismal stories
Do but themselves confound;
   His strength the more is.
No lion can him fright,
   He'll with a giant fight;
But he will have a right
   To be a pilgrim.

Hobgoblin nor foul fiend
   Can daunt his spirit;
He knows he at the end
   Shall life inherit.
Then fancies fly away,
   He'll fear not what men say;
He'll labour night and day
   To be a pilgrim.

(From *The Pilgrim's Progress*, Part II)

Meditations upon a candle

Man's like a candle in a candlestick,
Made up of tallow and a little wick;
And as the candle is before 'tis lighted,
Just such be they who are in sin benighted.
Nor can a man his soul with grace inspire,
More than can candles set themselves on fire.
Candles receive their light from what they are not;
Men, grace from Him, for whom at first they care not.

We manage candles when they take the fire;
God ruleth men, when grace doth them inspire.

As biggest candles give the better light,
So grace on biggest sinners shines most bright.
The candle shines to make another see;
A saint unto his neighbour light should be.
The blinking candle we do much despise;
Saints dim of light are high in no man's eyes.

Again, though it may seem to some a riddle,
We used to light our candle at the middle.
True, light doth at the candle's end appear,
And grace the heart first reaches by the ear;
But 'tis the wick the fire doth kindle on,
As 'tis the heart that grace first works upon.
Thus both do fasten upon what's the main,
And so their life and vigour do maintain.

As candles in the wind are apt to flare,
So Christians in a tempest do despair.
We see the flame with smoke attended is;
And in our holy lives there's much amiss.
Sometimes a thief will candle-light annoy:
And lusts do seek our graces to destroy.
What brackish is will make a candle sputter;
'Twixt sin and grace there's oft a heavy clutter.
Sometimes the light burns dim, 'cause of the snuff,
And sometimes 'tis extinguish'd with a puff:
But watchfulness preventeth both these evils,
Keeps candles light, and grace in spite of devils.
But let not snuffs nor puffs make us to doubt;
Our candle may be lighted, though puff'd out.

The candle in the night doth all excel,
Nor sun, nor moon, nor stars then shine so well:
So is the Christian in our hemisphere,
Whose light shows others how their course to steer.
When candles are put out all's in confusion;
Where Christians are not, devils make intrusion.

They then are happy who such candles have;
All others dwell in darkness and the grave.
But candles that do blink within the socket,
And saints whose eyes are always in their pocket,
Are much alike; such candles make us fumble;
And as such saints, good men and bad to stumble.
Good candles don't offend, except sore eyes,
Nor hurt, unless it be the silly flies.
How good are shining candles in the night!
How sweet is holy living for delight!

But let us draw toward the candle's end.
The fire, you see, doth wick and tallow spend;
So wastes man's life, until his glass is run,
And so the candle and the man are done.
The man now lays him down upon his bed;
The wick yields up its fire, and so is dead.
The candle now extinct is, but the man
By grace mounts up to glory, there to stand.

8

Sermons and Sayings

The Holy City

I saw a new heaven and a new earth: for the first heaven and the first earth were passed away; and there was no more sea. And I John saw the holy city, new Jerusalem, coming down from God out of heaven, prepared as a bride adorned for her husband. . . . And he carried me away in the spirit to a great and high mountain, and shewed me that great city, the holy Jerusalem, descending out of heaven from God, having the glory of God: and her light was like unto a stone most precious, even like a jasper stone, clear as crystal. . . . and the street of the city was pure gold, as it were transparent glass. (Revelation 21:1–2, 10–11, 21)

The saints are yet but an army routed, and are apt sometimes through fear, and sometimes through forgetfulness, to mistake the word of their Captain-General, the Son of God, and are also too prone to shoot and kill even their very right-hand man; but at that day all such doing shall be laid aside. It is darkness, and not light, that keeps God's people from knowing one another, both in their faith and language; and it is darkness that makes them stand at so great a distance both in judgment and affections, as in these and other days they have done.

Never was fair weather after foul – nor warm weather

after cold – nor a sweet and beautiful spring after a heavy, and nipping and terrible winter, so comfortable, sweet, desirable and welcome to the poor birds and beasts of the field, as this day will be to the church of God. Darkness! It was the plague of Egypt – it is an empty, forlorn, desolate, solitary and discomforting state. Wherefore light – the illuminating grace of God, especially in the measure that it will be communicated to us at this day – must be precious. In light there is warmth and pleasure; it is by the light of the sun that the whole universe appears to us distinctly, and it is by its heat that everything grows and flourishes. All this will now be gloriously and spiritually answered in this holy and new Jerusalem. Oh, how clearly will all the spiders, and dragons, and owls, and foul spirits of Anti-Christ at that day be revealed by the light! How also will all the pretty robins and little birds in the Lord's field most sweetly send forth their pleasant notes, and all the herbs and flowers of his garden spring.

You know how pleasant this is, even to be fulfilled in the letter of it, not only to birds and beasts, but men; especially it is pleasant to those men who have for several years been held in the chains of affliction. It must, therefore, be most pleasant and desirable to the afflicted church of Christ, which has now lain in the dungeon of Anti-Christ for above a thousand years.

Now this street, or way of holiness, is purposely called not many, but one, to show us the perfection of light, grace, faith and spiritual comfort, that the inhabitants will enjoy. Wherefore from this I gather that then all saints will walk in one street, in one way, and in one light. It is Anti-Christ that has brought in all those crossings, by-lanes and odd nooks, that to this day many an honest heart greatly loses itself in; but at this day they will be otherwise minded, that is, made all to savour one thing, and to walk one way, not biting and devouring each other as now. And indeed there is all reason it should be thus, for the street itself is but one.

By saying this street is gold, he would have us to understand the worth and treasure that is laid up in the ways of
God, and of a truly gracious heart. As the ways of God are
thus rich, and so far above the gold and rubies of this
world, so also is that sanctified and gracious heart without
which no man can walk in this golden street. It is not every
clown with his clumping dirty shoes that is admitted into
kings' privy chambers and private palaces; neither does
God, nor will he at the day of New Jerusalem, allow any to
trace about this golden street but such as have golden feet,
and that beautified with goodly shoes. As for this street, all
that walk in it must be golden men.

Seasonable Counsel, or Advice to Sufferers

When persecution is raised against a people, there is a
design laid for the ruin of those people's souls – something
that would destroy them. I am not so uncharitable as to
think that persecuting men design this. But I verily believe
that the Devil designs this when he stirs them up to so
sorry a work. Alas, men in their acts of this nature have
designs that are lower and of a more inferior rank! Some
of them look no higher than revenge upon the carcass –
than the spoiling of their neighbour of his estate, liberty or
life – than the greatening of themselves in this world by
the ruins of those they have power to spoil. Ay, but Satan
will not be put off like that! It is not a bag of money, or the
punishing of the carcass of such a people, that will please
or satisfy him. It is the soul that he aims at – the ruin of the
precious soul that he has bent himself to bring to pass.

Are you troubled and persecuted for your faith? Look to
it, the hand of Satan is in this thing; and whatever men
drive at by doing as they do, the Devil designs no less than
the damnation of your souls. "Ware hawk,' says the fal-
coner when the dogs are coming near her – especially if
she is too much minding her belly and too forgetful of
what the nature of the dog is.

When a tyrant goes to dispossess a neighbouring prince of what is lawfully his own, the men that he employs to overcome and get the land fight for half-crowns and the like and are content with their wages; but the tyrant is after the kingdom – nothing will serve him but the kingdom. This is the case: men when they persecute are after the stuff, but the Devil is after the soul; nor will anything less than that satisfy him. Let him then that is a sufferer commit the keeping of his soul to God, lest stuff and soul and all be lost at once.

Persecution sometimes follows God's people so hotly as to leave them nothing but a soul to care for. They have had no house, no land, no money, no goods, no life, no liberty to care for. All is gone but the soul. Goods have been confiscated, liberty has been in irons, the life condemned, the neck in a halter or the body in the fire. So, then, all has been done but their soul. Let them commit the keeping of their soul to God. Do not keep your soul in your own hand, for fear of losing that with the rest.

God is very willing to take the charge and care of the soul of them that suffer for his sake in the world. Act faith, trust God, believe his Word, and go on in your way of witness-bearing for him, and you will find all well and according to the desire of your heart at least. True, Satan will make it his business to tempt you to doubt this, that your way be made yet more hard and difficult. For he knows that unbelief is a soul-perplexing sin and makes that which would otherwise be light, pleasant and easy, unutterably heavy and burdensome to the sufferer.

'But I am in the dark.' I answer, Never stick at that. It is most bravely done to trust God with my soul in the dark, and resolve to serve God for nothing, rather than give up. Not to see, and yet to believe, and yet to be uncertain what we shall have at last, argues love, fear, faith, and an honest mind. Your own natural weakness and timorousness will not overcome you. For it will not be too hard for God. God can make the most soft-spirited man as hard as adamant –

harder than flint, harder than the northern steel. He can turn you into another man, and make you something you never were.

To commit the keeping of the soul to God, if it is done in faith and prayer, brings this holy boldness and confidence into the soul. Suppose a man in the country had to go to London, and had a great charge of money to pay in there – suppose, also, that the way there was exceeding dangerous because of the highwaymen that continually stay there – what now must this man do to go on his journey cheerfully? Why, let him pay in his money to such a person in the country as will be sure to return it for him at London safely. Why, this is the case – you are bound for heaven, but the way there is dangerous. It is beset everywhere with evil angels, who would rob you of your soul. What now? Why, if you want to go on your dangerous journey cheerfully, commit your treasure – your soul – to God to keep. And then you may say with comfort, 'Well, that care is over; for whatever I meet with on my way there, my soul is safe enough. The thieves, if they meet me, cannot get at that. I know to whom I have committed my soul, and I am persuaded that he will keep that to my joy and everlasting comfort.'

It is possible for Christians to suffer for evil-doing – it is possible for them to be brought to public justice for their faults – and therefore let Christians beware. Though the Christian is the only man at liberty (as called to it by God), yet his liberty is limited to things that are good. He is not licensed thereby to indulge the flesh. Holiness and liberty are joined together – our call to liberty is a call to holiness. A quiet and peaceable life in our respective places, under the government, is what we should pray for – that is, that we may, without molestation (if it is the will of God), spend our days in all godliness among our neighbours. We are bidden to give thanks to God for all men – for kings and all that are in authority. There is no man with whom we have to do, if we do as we should, who does not bring some good thing to us, or does some good thing for us. We will now descend from them that are in supreme authority and will come to inferior men. Suppose some of them to act beyond measure, cruelly. Can no good come to us out of this? Do not even such things as are most bitter to the flesh tend to awaken Christians to faith and prayer – to a sight of the emptiness of this world and the fadingness of the best it yields? Does not God by these things often call our sins to remembrance and provoke us to amendment of life? How then can we be offended at things by which we reap so much good and at things that God makes so profitable for us?

Since it is required of us that we give thanks to God for all these men, it follows that we submit with quietness to whatever God does to us through them. I will then love them, bless them, pray for them and do them good. I speak now of the men that hurt me. We need all, and more than all, that has yet befallen us.

If you are captured, do not be offended at God or man – not at God, for you are his servant, your life and your all are his – not at man, for he is God's rod, and is ordained in this to do you good. Have you escaped? Laugh. Are you captured? Laugh. I mean, be pleased whichever way things go, for the scales are still in God's hand.

Is it not amazing to see one poor inconsiderable man, in a spirit of faith and patience, overcome all the threatenings, cruelties, afflictions and sorrows that a whole world can lay upon him? None can quail him, none can crush him, none can bend down his spirit. None can make him forsake what he has received from God – a commandment to stand fast.

A Discourse Upon The Pharisee and the Publican

It is strange to see, and yet it is seen, that men cross in their minds, cross in their principles, cross in their apprehensions, and cross in their prayers, too, should yet meet in

the temple to pray. The Pharisee carried the bell and wore
the garland for religion; the publican was counted vile and
base and reckoned among the worst of men, just as our
informers and bum-bailiffs are with us at this day. The
publican was a Jew, but he fell in with the heathen and
took the advantage of their tyranny to probe and
impoverish his brothers. The one was an open *outside* sinner, the other a filthy *inside* one. The Pharisee prayed with
himself, said Christ. It is at this day amazingly common for
men to pray extempore also. To pray by a book, by a pre-
meditated set form, is now out of fashion. He is counted
nobody now who cannot at any moment, at a minute's
warning, make a prayer of half an hour long. I am not
against extempore prayer, for I believe it to be the best
kind of praying; but yet I fear that there are a great many
such prayers made, especially in pulpits and public meetings, without the breathing of the Holy Spirit in them. For
if a Pharisee of old could do so, why may not a Pharisee do
the same now? Intelligence and reason and notion is now
screwed up to a very great height; nor do men lack words
or ideas, or pride, to make them do this thing. Great is the
formality of religion this day and little is its power.

The Pharisee prayed with himself. God and the Pharisee
were not together, there was only the Pharisee and himself. How many times have I heard ancient men and
ancient women at it with themselves, when all alone in
some private room or in some solitary path; and in their
chat they have been sometimes reasoning, sometimes chid-
ing, sometimes pleading, sometimes praying, and sometimes singing; but still all have been done by themselves
when all alone. So the Pharisee was at it with himself, *he*
and *himself* performed the duty of prayer at this time.
'God,' he says, 'thank you that I am not like other men.' I
remember that Luther used to say, 'In the name of God
begins all mischief.' All must be fathered upon God —
'God, thank you' is on the persecutor's lips, is the burden
of the heretic's song, is in every man's mouth, and must be

entailed to every error, delusion and damnable doctrine that is in the world.

But since, blind Pharisee, you are so confident that your state is good, when did you begin to be righteous? Was it before or after you had been a sinner? What does it mean, this preferring of your own rules, laws, statutes, ordinances and appointments before the rules, laws, statutes, ordinances and appointments of God? What kind of righteousness shall this be called? Whose back will such a suit of clothes fit, that is set together just cross and thwart to what it should be? And will you call this your righteousness? Will you stand in this, plead for this, and venture an eternal concern in such a piece of linsey-woolsey as this? O fools and blind! It was partly for the sake of my own good deeds that I obtained mercy to be in heaven and glory; shall *this* be the burden of the song of heaven? Or is this what is composed by that glittering heavenly host, and which we have read of in the holy book of God? No, no, that song runs upon other feet, stands in far better strains, being composed of far higher and truly heavenly matter. You have set yourself against God in a way of contending; you will not bate God an ace of what your righteousness is worth, and will also make it worth what you yourself decide. Pharisee, I will assure you, you are beside the saddle; your state is not good. A man must be good before he can do good, and evil before he can do evil; for a tree must be a sweeting tree before it yields sweetings; and a crab tree before it yields crabs.

And now see how thwart and cross the Pharisee and the publican lay to one another in the temple. The Pharisee goes in boldly, the publican stands behind, aloof, as one not worthy to approach the divine presence; the Pharisee has many fine things with which he strokes himself over the head, and in effect calls himself one of God's white boys – and that in God's presence – but alas, poor publican, your guilt stops your mouth: you have not one good thing to say of yourself. What will you do, publican, what will you do? Call all the world to be silent; let the angels of God come near and listen; for the publican has come to have to do with God! 'He beat his breast, saying God have mercy on me a sinner.' This wisdom has outdone the Pharisee, for it is better for us to apply to God's mercy than to trust to ourselves that we are righteous. The publican hit the mark – he got nearer to and more *into* the heart of God and his Son than did the Pharisee.

Come and Welcome to Jesus Christ

Him that cometh to me I will in no wise cast out. (John 6:37)

There are two sorts of sinners that are coming to Jesus Christ. First, the one who has never come before; second, the one who came formerly, and after that went back, but has since bethought himself, and is now coming again. Both these sorts of sinners are intended by him in the text, as is evident because both are not the coming sinners.

1. For the first of these – the sinner that has never begun to come – his way is more easy. I do not say it is more plain and open for coming to Christ than is the other – those last not having the clog of a guilty conscience, for the sin of backsliding. But all the encouragement of the gospel, and with what invitations are contained in it to coming sinners, are as free and as open to the one as to the other; so that they may with the same freedom and liberty, as from the Word, both alike claim interest in the promise. 'Whoever is thirsty, let him come' (Revelation 22:17).

2. That the backslider is intended is evident because he is sent to by name: 'Go, tell his disciples and Peter' (Mark 16:7). But Peter was a godly man. True, but he was also a backslider, a desperate backslider: he had denied his Master once, twice, three times, cursing and swearing that he did not know him.

Again, when David had backslidden, and had committed adultery and murder in his backsliding, he must be sent to by name: 'And,' the text says, 'the Lord sent Nathan to David.' And he sent him to tell him, after he had brought him to unfeigned acknowledgement, 'The Lord has forgiven your sins' (2 Samuel 12:1, 13).

This man also was far gone; he took a man's wife, and killed her husband, and endeavoured to cover all with wicked dissimulation.

But I am a great sinner, you say.

'I will in no wise cast out,' says Christ.

But I am an old sinner, you say.

'I will in no wise cast out,' says Christ.

But I am a hard-hearted sinner, you say.

'I will in no wise cast out,' says Christ.

But I am a backsliding sinner, you say.

'I will in no wise cast out,' says Christ.

But I have served Satan all my days, you say.

'I will in no wise cast out,' says Christ.

But I have sinned against light, you say.

'I will in no wise cast out,' says Christ.

But I have sinned against mercy, you say.

'I will in no wise cast out,' says Christ.

But I have no good thing to bring with me, you say.

'I will in no wise cast out,' says Christ.

The Water of Life

It is a deep river. As this river is deep, so it is wide and broad. It is broader than the sea – a river that cannot be passed over. If you can swim, here you may roll up and down as the fishes do in the sea. Nor need you fear drowning in this river; it will bear you up and carry you over the highest hills.

Just as this river is deep, broad and full, so it still abounds with water. This river of water of life, which is also signified by these waters, is a river that abounds and that overflows its banks in an infinite and unspeakable manner. A river is water that is common – common in the streams, though otherwise in the head. As it is a river, it is common and of common use and for common good.

Though a river, in the streams of it, is common, yet a river as it passes through a country or province will choose its own way; it will run in the valleys, in the plains, not over steeples and hills. It will also fetch its compasses and circuits; it will go about and reach hither and thither; and according to its courses it will miss by its turnings what places and people it chooses. Yet it is common, for it lies open; it is common for all the beasts of the field. There is therefore a difference to be put between the commonness of a thing and its presence. A thing may be common, yet far enough off from you. Epsom, Tunbridge Wells and Bath may be common, but yet a great way off from some that have need of them. The same may be said of this river – it is common in the streams, but it runs its own circuit and keeps its own water-courses. It runs in the midst of the valleys to water the humble and the lowly. Therefore anyone who is thirsty and wants to drink is told to come down to the waters. They are common, but you must come to them where they are, or you will be no better off for them.

Just as this river is said to be pure, so it is said to be clear. Clear is to be taken as meaning light, daylight, sunlight; for, indeed, it is never day or sunshine with the soul until the streams of this river come gliding to our doors, into our houses, into our hearts. Clear is set in opposition to that which is not pleasing; for to be clear is to be pleasant. I read of rivers that looked red as blood, that stank like the blood of a dead man; but this is no such river. I read of rivers whose streams are like streams of brimstone, fiery streams, streams of burning pitch; but this is none of them.

These are the waters that the doves love to sit by; because by the clearness of these streams they can see their pretty selves, as in a glass. These are the streams where the doves wash their eyes, and by which they solace themselves and take great content. As in fair waters a man may see the body of the sun, and of the moon, and of the stars, and the very body of heaven; so he that stands upon the bank of this river, and that washes his eyes with this water, may see the Son of God, the glory of God, and the habitation that God has prepared for his people. Are not these pleasant sights? Is not this excellent water? Has not this river pleasant streams?

There are many, nowadays, that want to invent waters to drink for the health of the body, and to allure those that are ill to buy. They will praise their waters beyond their worth, and if they are helpful to one person in a hundred, they make as if they could cure everyone. Well, here you have the great Physician himself with his water, and he calls it the water of life – water of life for the soul. This water has been tested times without number; it never fails but when it is not taken. No disease comes amiss to it; it cures blindness, deadness, deafness, dumbness; it will drive away devils and spirits; it will cure enchantments and witchcrafts; it will dissolve doubts and mistrusts, though they are grown as hard as stone in the heart. It will make you have a white soul, and that is better than to have a white skin.

This river is the running out of God's heart. This is his heart and soul. Wherefore forbear your mistrusts, cast off your slavish fears, hang your misgivings as to this upon the hedge; and believe you have an invitation sufficient for it. A river is before your face. And as to your lack of goodness and works, let that by no means daunt you. This is a river of water of life – streams of grace and mercy. There is enough in it to help you, for grave brings all that is lacking to the soul. Therefore, you have nothing to do but to drink and live for ever.

Bunyan's Last Sermon

Which were born, not of blood, nor of the will of the flesh, nor of the will of man, but of God. (John 1:13)

[John Brown writes that on 19 August 1688 'Bunyan was preaching at Mr Gamman's meeting, near Whitechapel, what proved to be his last sermon. It was . . . shortly afterwards printed, not from any manuscript of the preacher's, but from the notes of some hearer who was present. According to this report there was one passage in this sermon which was indeed the fitting close to the ministry of a man so catholic and large-hearted as we know this preacher was. "Do you see a soul that has the image of God in him?" he asked. "Love him, love him: say, 'This man and I must go to heaven one day'; serve one another, do good for one another; and if any wrong you, pray to God to right you, and love the brotherhood." If we may trust this report, and there is no reason why we should not, the last words that John Bunyan ever uttered from the pulpit were words that nobly expressed the spirit of his own life. They were these: "Be holy in all manner of conversation. Consider that the holy God is your Father, and let this oblige you to live like the children of God, that you may look your Father in the face with comfort another day."]

A child, before it is born into the world, is in the dark dungeon of its mother's womb: so a child of God, before he is born again, is in the dark dungeon of sin, sees nothing of the kingdom of God; therefore it is called a new birth: the same soul has love one way in its carnal condition, another way when it is born again.

A child, you know, is incident to cry as soon as it comes into the world; for if there is no noise, they say it is dead. You that are born of God and Christians, if you are no criers, there is no spiritual life in you – if you are born of God, you are crying ones; as soon as he has raised you out of the dark dungeon of sin, you cannot but cry to God, 'What must I do to be saved?'

It is not only natural for a child to cry, but it must crave the breast; it cannot live without the breast – therefore Peter makes it the true trial of a new-born babe: the newborn babe desires the sincere milk of the Word, that he may grow thereby.

The child that is newly born, if it has no other comforts to keep it warm than it had in its mother's womb, it dies; it must have something got for its succour. So Christ had swaddling clothes prepared for him; so those that are born again, they must have some promise of Christ to keep them alive; those that are in a carnal state, they warm themselves with other things. What fine things has Christ prepared to wrap all in that are born again! This is set out nothing in the world but the righteousness of Christ and the graces of the Spirit, without which a newborn babe cannot live, unless they have the righteousness of Christ.

There is usually some similarity between the father and the child. It may be the child looks like its father; so those that are born again have a new similarity – they have the image of Christ (Galatians 4). Everyone that is born of God has something of the features of heaven upon him.

Children, it is natural for them to depend upon their father for what they need; if they need a pair of shoes, they go and tell him; if they need food, they go and tell him; so should the child of God do. Do you need spiritual food? Go tell God of it. Do you need strength of grace? Ask it of God. Do you need strength against temptations? Go and tell God of it. When the devil tempts you, run home and tell your heavenly Father – go pour out your complaints to God.

Mr John Bunyan's Dying Sayings

[William Henry Harding writes: 'The tiny book entitled *Mr John Bunyan's Dying Sayings*, a collection of aphorisms, gathered perhaps by Cockayn, and classified under appropriate headings, demonstrates that the great themes which were the staple of his conversation in life dominated and illuminated his thoughts even to the end.']

Sin
If sin be so dreadful a thing as to wring the heart of the Son of God, how shall a poor wretched sinner be able to bear it?

Affliction
If we heartily renounced the pleasures of the world, we should be very little troubled as to our afflictions; that which renders an afflicted state so insupportable to many is that they are too much addicted to the pleasures of this life, and so cannot endure that which makes a separation between them.

Repentance
Repentance carries with it a divine rhetoric, and persuades Christ to forgive multitudes of sins committed against him.

Prayer
Prayer will make a man cease from sin, or sin will entice a man to cease from prayer. The spirit of prayer is more precious than treasures of gold and silver. Pray often, for prayer is a shield to the soul, a sacrifice to God, and a scourge for Satan.

Suffering
It is not every suffering that makes a martyr, but suffering for the Word of God, after a right manner; that is, not only for righteousness, but for righteousness' sake; not only for

truth, but out of love to truth; not only for God's Word, but according to it; to wit, in that holy, humble, meek manner, as the Word of God requires.

The joys of heaven

Christ is the desire of nations, the joy of angels, the delight of the Father; what solace then must that soul be filled with, that has the possession of him to all eternity. If you want to be better satisfied what the beatific vision means, my request is that you would live holily, and go and see.

The Acceptable Sacrifice

The sacrifices of God are a broken spirit: a broken and a contrite heart, O God, thou wilt not despise. (Psalm 51:17)

The broken heart is hard to bear, for soul-pain is the sorest pain. With such a man God has wrestled and given him a fall, and now he crouches and cringes and craves for mercy. Like one with a broken limb who so far from hectoring it with a man is afraid lest even a child should touch him, so he begs of God to deal with him with tender hands. Once, being at an honest woman's house, I after some pause asked her how she did. 'Very badly,' was her reply; 'I am afraid I shall not be saved.' Breaking out with a heavy heart she said, 'Ah, good Mr Bunyan! Christ and a pitcher; if I had Christ though I went and begged my bread with a pitcher, it would be better with me than I think it is now.' This woman had her heart broken, she wanted Christ. This cry of 'Christ and a pitcher' made a melodious noise in the ears of the very angels. At first our pride is laid low. If a man is proud of his strength or manhood, a broken leg will maul him; and if a man is proud of his goodness a broken heart will maul him. Yet a broken heart or a contrite spirit is a heaven-sent blessing. If you have it, God is giving you what he himself is pleased with;

he has given you a cabinet to hold his grace in, he has given you a heart that can heartily desire his salvation, a heart after his own heart, that is, such as suits his mind. True it is painful now, sorrowful now, penitent now, grieved now; now it is broken, now it bleeds, now it sobs, now it sighs, now it mourns and cries to God. Well, very well; all this is because he has a mind to make you laugh; he has made you sorry on earth that you may rejoice in heaven. Covet a broken heart, prize a contrite spirit: I say, covet it now, now the white flag is hung out, now the golden sceptre of grace is held out to you. It is wounding work, of course, this breaking of the hearts, but without wounding there is no saving. Conversion is not the smooth, easy-going process some men seem to think it, otherwise man's heart would never have been compared to fallow ground and God's word to a plough. The fallow ground must be ploughed and ploughed, and even after that be soundly harrowed, else there will be but slender harvest. To the same purport is that other analogy of grafting, for where there is grafting there is cutting, the scion must be let in with a wound; to stick on to the outside or to tie it on with a string would be of no use. Heart must be set to heart and back to back, or there will be no sap from root to branch, and this, I say, must be done by a wound. Men are too lofty, too proud, too wild, too devilishly resolved in the ways of their own destruction. Nothing will hinder them from ruining their own precious and immortal souls but the breaking of their hearts.